Interactive Genetics

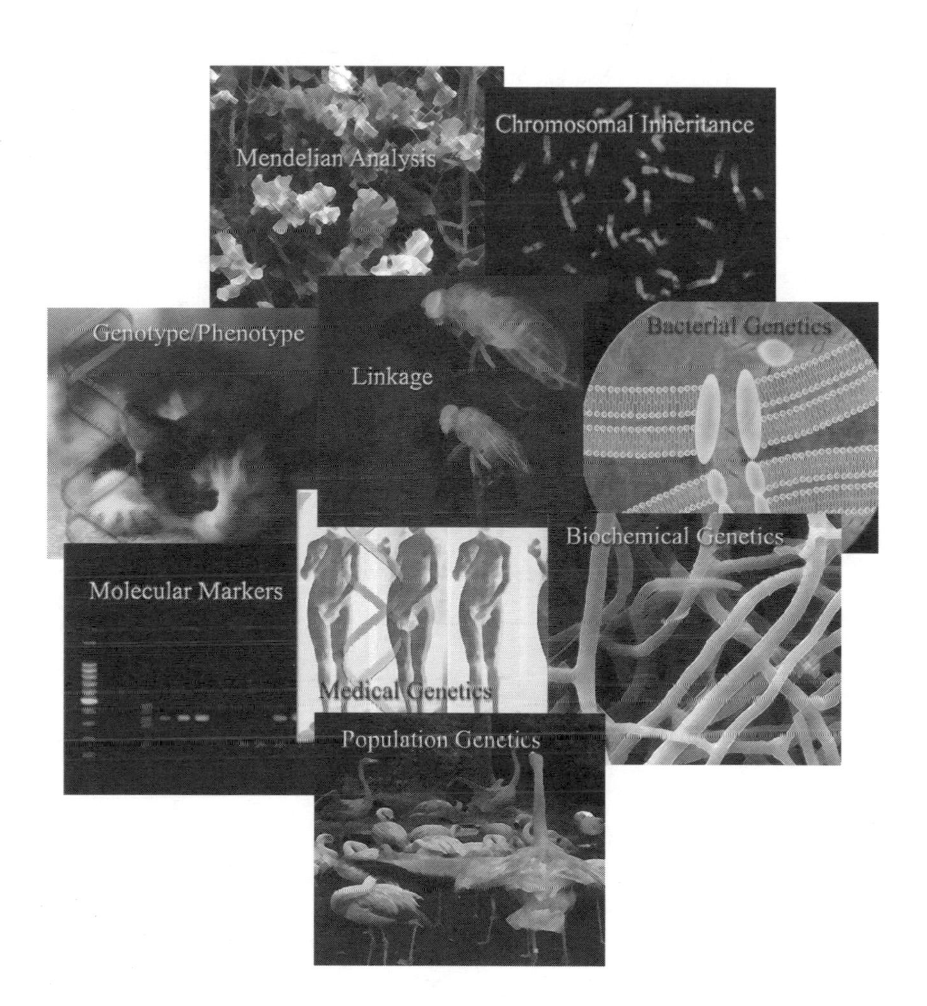

Lianna Johnson
John Merriam

Copyright © 2005 by Lianna Johnson and John Merriam

Our special thanks to Atila van Nas for providing illustrations and artwork for this edition.

All rights reserved.

Permission in writing must be obtained from the publisher before any part of this work may be reproduced or transmitted in any form or by any means, electronic or mechanical, including photocopying and recording, or by any information storage or retrieval system.

Printed in the United States of America.

10 9 8 7 6 5 4 3 2 1

ISBN 0-7380-1546-6

Hayden-McNeil Publishing, Inc.
14903 Pilot Drive
Plymouth, MI 48170
www.hmpublishing.com

Johnson 1546-6 W05 Interactive Genetics

Detailed Table of Contents

Mendelian Analysis

Goals for Mendelian Analysis:

1. Describe the mode of inheritance of a phenotypic difference between two strains.
   - Distinguish dominance and recessive in traits
   - Determine whether the phenotype difference is due to a single gene with two alleles
   - Write genotypes and predict phenotypes
   - Predict the number of possible gamete types, their kinds and ratios
2. Distinguish self crosses from test crosses
3. Apply these concepts to simple human pedigrees for select traits
   - Calculate probabilities using product and sum rules
   - Use the binomial expansion to calculate the combinations of possible outcomes

Mendelian Problems

Problem 1

Let's begin with a simple cross between two pure breeding peas, a purple flowered pea and a white flowered pea. How many traits or characters are different between the purple and white parents?

In this cross the pollen from the purple parent is used to fertilize the ovules of the white parent. How many genetically distinct gametes are produced from the purple parent?

How many genetically distinct gametes does the white flowered parent produce?

All the progeny of the parental cross are purple flowered pea plants. However, when these peas are self crossed, both purple and white peas appear in the next or F2 generation. Which phenotype is the dominant phenotype?

Using A and a to designate the different forms of the inherited trait (alleles), assign genotypes to the three generations of the cross described above. How many genetically distinct gametes are produced from the F1? In the simple Punnett Square shown below, fill in the genotype of the progeny using A/a.

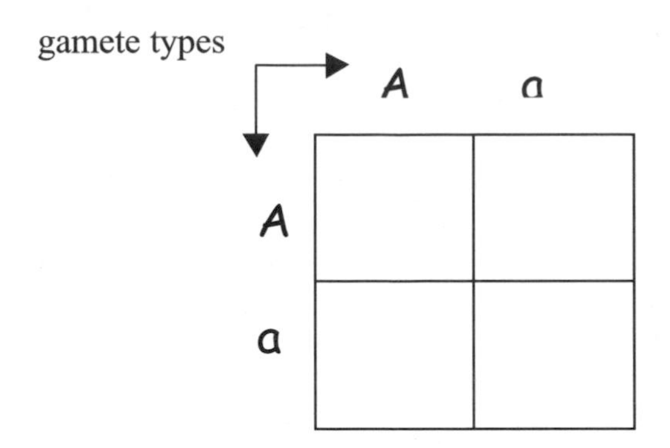

Indicate the phenotype expected for each genotype in the Punnett Square above. What is the ratio of purple flowered progeny to white flowered progeny in the F2?

What genotypic ratios would you predict?

Problem 2

The grass tree is the common name for the Australian genus *Xanthorrhoea* in the lily family, *Liliaceae.* Grass trees grow to a height of about 4.5m (15 feet) and bear long, narrow leaves in a tuft at the top of the trunk. White flowers or yellow flowers can be produced in a dense spike above the leaves in a given tree. A tree producing yellow flowers was self crossed. The seeds were collected and planted to determine flower color of each progeny tree. 28 trees were found to produce yellow flowers and 8 trees were found to produce white flowers.

What is the expected genetic (phenotypic) ratio of yellow flowering grass trees to white flowering grass trees among the progeny?

Which phenotype is dominant, white or yellow flowering trees?

Using the symbols of Y/y, write the genotypes of the original yellow flowering tree and the progeny.

Yellow x Yellow

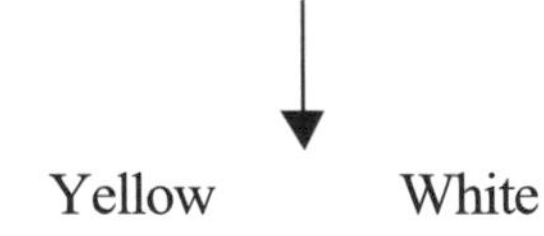

Yellow White

Predict the phenotypic ratios for the crosses shown below:

Cross	Phenotypic Ratios	
	Yellow	White
White tree x White tree		
Original Yellow tree x White tree		
Pure Breeding Yellow tree x White tree		
Original Yellow tree self crossed		

Problem 3

Two pure breeding strains of peas, one giving wrinkled, yellow seeds and the other round, green seeds, were crossed and all the resulting peas were round and yellow. These round seeds were then planted and the flowers self fertilized. The peas produced from this selfing contained four phenotypic classes.

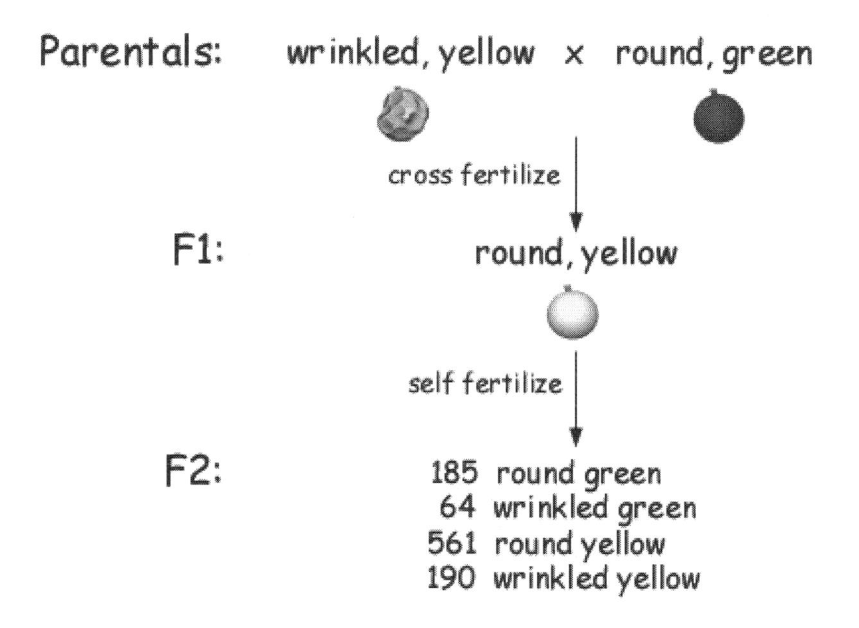

How many traits or characters are different between the pure breeding parents?

Using A and a to designate pea shape and B and b to designate pea color, assign genotypes to the three generations in the diagram of the cross above.

How many genetically distinct gametes are produced from the F1?
Fill out the Punnett Square shown below.

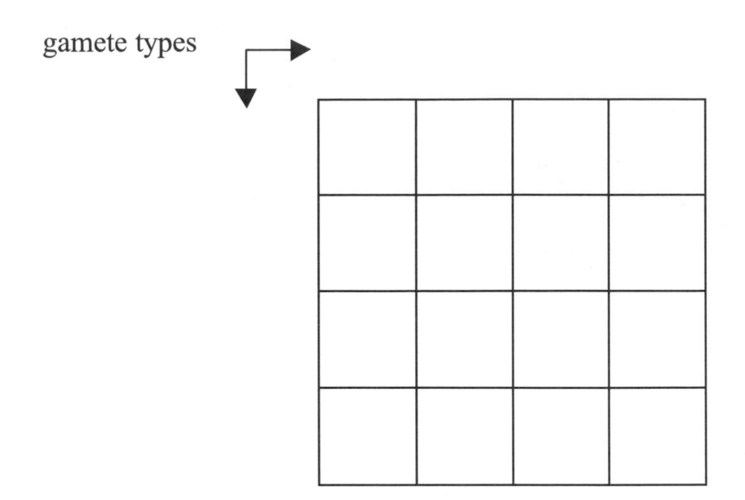

How many genotypes above correspond to the round and yellow phenotype?

How many genotypes above correspond to the wrinkled yellow phenotype?

How many genotypes above correspond to the round green phenotype?

How many genotypes above give rise to a green wrinkled pea?

Using the Punnett square above, what is the ratio of round peas to wrinkled peas (ignore the color)?

What is the ratio for yellow versus green?

Determine the ratio of round yellow peas to round green peas to wrinkled yellow peas to wrinkled green peas expected from this dihybrid cross.

Problem 4

You have been sent to Planet TATACCA to conduct basic genetic experiments on a new species: **X**. The 2 traits that you are observing are the shape and attachment of the ear. Pointy ears are dominant to round, and attached ear lobes are dominant to detached. Assuming that genes responsible for these phenotypes assort independently, write out the genotype of the parents in each of the crosses. Assume homozygosity unless there is evidence otherwise. **P** and **R** stand for the pointy and rounded phenotypes, respectively, and **A** and **D** stand for the attached and detached phenotypes. Use *P* and *p* for the pointy and round ear alleles and *A* and *a* for the attached and detached.

Parental Genotype	Parental Phenotype	Number of Progeny			
		PA	PD	RA	RD
	PA x PA	447	152	147	50
	PA x PD	107	98	0	0
	PA x RA	95	0	91	0
	RA x RA	0	0	153	48
	PD x PD	0	149	0	51
	PA x PA	140	46	0	0
	PA x PD	151	147	48	50

Problem 5

Geneticists working with the common fruit fly, *Drosophila melanogaster*, are studying the mode of inheritance of vestigial wings. Vestigial wings are a mutant phenotype in which wing development is curtailed. Wildtype or normal flies display normal wing development. Geneticists working with flies label genes and the alleles, and therefore the flies, after the mutant phenotype. Pure breeding vestigial flies have the genotype of *vgvg* (two copies of the mutant allele) and the phenotype is denoted as vg for vestigial. Pure breeding normal flies are denoted vg^+vg^+ for their genotype and their phenotype is described as vg^+.

After sorting flies for several hours, a freshman volunteering in the laboratory accidentally sneezes, mixing up all three piles of flies. Originally, one pile of flies displayed vestigial wings, a second pile of flies had normal wings but was heterozygous, and the third pile had normal wings and was homozygous. The principal investigator of the laboratory calls on you, as an expert geneticist, to resort the flies. By performing several crosses, you are able to determine from which pile each fly originated.

Which phenotype is recessive, vestigial wings or wildtype wings? (See the table below).

Using the symbols of *vg+* and *vg*, write the genotypes of the flies used in each cross in the table below.

Genotype	Phenotype	Number of Progeny	
		vg+	*vg*
	Normal x Normal	628	209
	Vestigial x Normal	333	340
	Normal x Vestigial	454	0
	Vestigial x Vestigial	0	121
	Normal x Normal	92	0

Problem 6

One day as you were traveling along a semi deserted highway, your car has an electrical surge and suddenly stops. You can't get your car to run again so you decide to get out and walk to the nearest phone to call for a tow truck. While you are walking you see a dairy farm in the distance. As you get closer you notice that these are not ordinary cattle. Then, you see the signs indicating a government research facility. Because you are extremely interested in the genetics of these odd cows, you take a few with you as you run off. Amazingly, you and your new bovines have made it to your family's farm safely. You decide to breed the cattle to obtain a better understanding of the genetic basis for their coat color. The results from your crosses are found on the table below.

Parental Genotypes	Parental Phenotypes	Green Progeny	Purple Progeny
	Purple x Purple	0	98
	Green x Green	94	0
	Purple x Green	51	49
	Purple x Green	97	0
	Green x Green	71	27

Which color results from possessing a dominant allele?

Using *G* and *g* as allele designations in the form of *Gg* x *Gg*, assign the most probable genotypes for the parents in each cross above. Assume homozygosity unless there is evidence otherwise.

Besides having either a purple or a green coat, your cattle have two other odd traits that you have observed to be inherited in a Mendelian manner. Your new bovines have either yellow eyes (Y) or blue eyes (B) and produce either regular white milk (W) or chocolate milk (C). Consider the table below, which is the recessive eye color?

What type of milk is produced when a cow possesses a dominant allele?

Parental Phenotypes	Blue Chocolate	Yellow Chocolate	Blue White	Yellow White
BC x BC	10	4	3	1
BW x YC	7	8	0	0
BC x BW	4	0	3	0
BW x BW	0	0	15	5
YC x YC	0	22	0	7
BC x BC	12	4	0	0
BC x YC	10	11	3	4

Using *C* to indicate the allele for Chocolate milk production, *c* for white milk production, *B* for blue eyes and *b* to indicate the allele for yellow eyes, write the parental genotypes for each of the crosses shown above. Assume homozygosity unless there is evidence otherwise.

What proportion of the offspring of two parental cattle each of the genotype *Gg Bb Cc* (green with blue eyes and chocolate milk producing) will be *Gg bb cc*?

Consider the following cross: *Gg Bb Cc* x *gg Bb cc*

What fraction of the progeny do you expect to phenotypically resemble the first parent?

If 100 progeny resulted from crosses such as this, how many would you expect to exhibit new genotypes (i.e. do not genotypically resemble either parent)?

Pedigree & Probabilities

Problem 1

Part a. For the pedigree shown below, state whether the condition depicted by darkened symbols is dominant or recessive. Assume the trait is rare. Assign genotypes for all individuals using A/a designations.

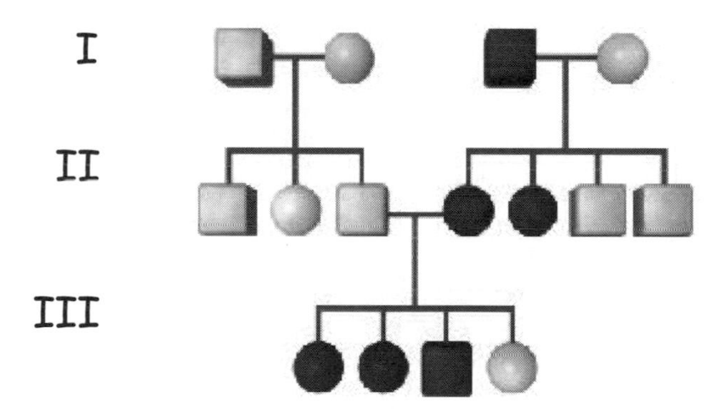

Part b. Assume the inherited trait depicted in the pedigree below is rare and state whether the condition is dominant or recessive. Assign genotypes for all individuals using A/a designations.

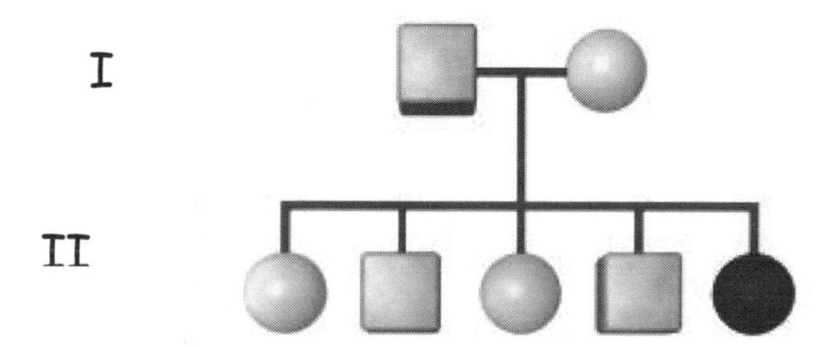

Part c. Is the pedigree shown below consistent with a dominant or recessive trait?

In analyzing this pedigree, would you conclude that this trait is caused by a rare or common allele?

Assign allele designations using A/a.

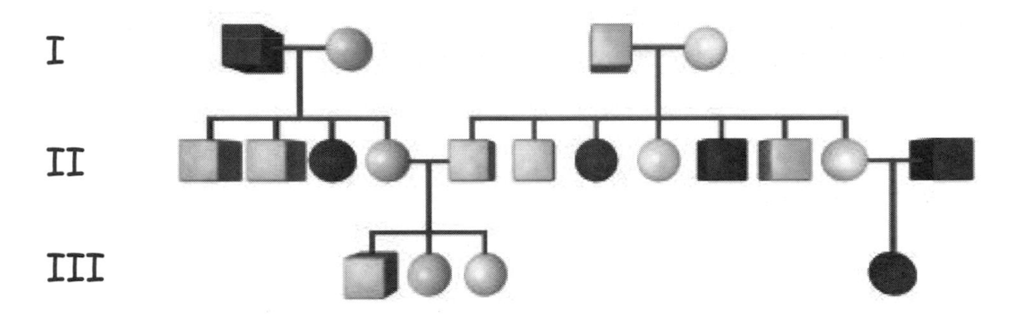

Problem 2

You have a single six-sided die. What is the chance of rolling a six?

What is the chance you will roll a five or a six? (HINT: Should you use the product rule or the sum rule to determine the probability of rolling one or the other?)

You are now given 2 additional dice. If you roll all three dice simultaneously, what is the chance of obtaining a 5 on all three dice?

Rolling your three dice again, what is the chance of obtaining no fives at all?

What is the chance of obtaining 2 fours and 1 three on any of the dice in a single roll?

What is the chance of obtaining the same number on all three dice?

What is the chance of rolling a different number on all three dice?

Problem 3

Preparing for a long night studying genetics, you open a big bag of candy coated peanuts. Two friends are supposed to join you so, you divide the bag into thirds. As you wait, you get hungry. But since you want to keep the bowls equal, you eat one from each bowl.

Bowl 1	**Bowl 2**	**Bowl 3**
30 blue candies	40 blue candies	30 blue candies
30 yellow candies	50 yellow candies	20 yellow candies
40 brown candies	10 green candies	50 red candies

What is the chance that you will select 3 blue candies?

What is the probability of selecting a brown, a green and a red candy?

If you pick one candy from each bowl, what is the chance you will pick 2 blue candies and a yellow candy?

If you pick one candy from each bowl, what is the probability of obtaining no yellow candies?

If you pick one candy from each bowl, what is the chance of picking at least one yellow?

The probability of having two peanuts in a single candy is 2%. If you eat 300 candies, how many double peanuts do you expect to find?

Problem 4

The ability to taste the chemical phenylthiocarbamide (PTC) is an autosomal dominant phenotype. Lori, a taster woman marries Russell, a taster man. Lori's father and her first child, Nicholas, are both nontasters.

What is the probability their second child will be a nontaster girl?

What is the probability their second child will be a taster boy?

What is the probability that their next two children will be nontaster girls?

Problem 5

A rare recessive allele inherited in a Mendelian manner causes phenylketonuria (PKU), which can lead to mental retardation if untreated. Fortunately, with a diet low in phenylalanine and tyrosine supplementation, normal development and lifespan are possible. Mike, a phenotypically normal man whose father had PKU marries Carol, a phenotypically normal woman whose brother had the disorder. The couple want to have a large family and come to you for advice on the probability that their children will have PKU.

What is the probability that the couple's first child will have PKU?

Their first child, Greg, has PKU and the couple wants to have five additional children. What is the probability that out of the their next five children only two will have PKU?

What is the possibility that they have no more than one affected child in the five additional children they are planning?

Problem 6

John and Maggie are expecting a child. John's great grandmother (mother's lineage) and Maggie's brother have a rare autosomal recessive condition. What is the chance that their child will be affected?

John and Maggie have just discovered they are going to have twins. What is the chance that both twins will be affected if they are identical twins?

If the twins are dizygotic twins (non identical or two egg twins), what is the chance they will both be affected?

If they are dizygotic twins, what is the chance that at least one of them will be affected?

Chromosomal Theory of Inheritance

Goals for Chromosomal Inheritance:

1. Understand the classical evidence that genes are located on chromosomes
   - Similarity of behavior of chromosomes in divisions with the behavior of genes (alleles) in inheritance.
   - Identification of genes with sex-linked inheritance and chromosomes with sex-linked inheritance
2. Distinguish mitosis from meiosis figures as well as the species diploid chromosome number by inspection of simple diagrams with chromosome size, shape, and copy number as the cues.
3. Connect genetic inheritance with chromosome behavior during divisions
   - Assign alleles to chromosomes: sister chromatids have identical alleles, homologous chromosomes (in a heterozygote) have different alleles
   - Homologous chromosomes pair and disjoin from each other in the first meiotic division, illustrating segregation of the alternate alleles.
   - Sister chromatids separate at mitosis, illustrating the constancy of the genotype in both daughter cells.
   - Genes that are on different chromosome pairs, i.e. non-homologous pairs, always assort independently.
4. Be able to identify sex-linked inheritance in a pedigree.

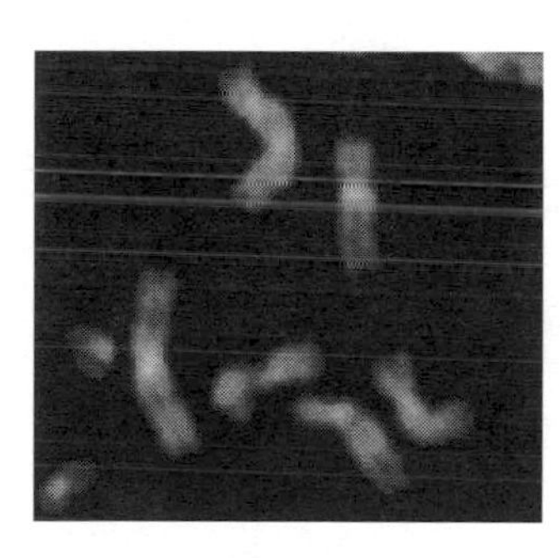

Mitosis and Meiosis

Problem 1

Many cells undergo a continuous alternation between division and nondivision. The interval between each mitotic division is called interphase. Which stages (G1, S, G2 or M) make up interphase?

It was once thought that the biochemical activity during interphase was devoted solely to cell growth and specific functions the cell normally performs. However, it is now known that another biochemical step critical to the next mitosis occurs during interphase: the replication of the DNA of each chromosome. During which stage of the cell cycle is DNA replicated?

The concentration of DNA contained in a single set of chromosomes is frequently referred to as "c". Diploid somatic cells have two sets of chromosomes and alternate between 2c and 4c. A cell has 2c before DNA replication. Then, it has twice that amount, 4c, until it undergoes mitotic division. After mitosis, the two resulting cells will both have 2c.

The job of the mitotic division phase is to segregate the replicated chromosomes into two cells, each with the same chromosome and genetic complement as the parent cell. The four phases of mitosis are: prophase, metaphase, anaphase and telophase.

DNA replication (in S phase) produces a second double helix. During prophase, the sister double helices condense, forming the X shaped chromosomes typically seen under the microscope.

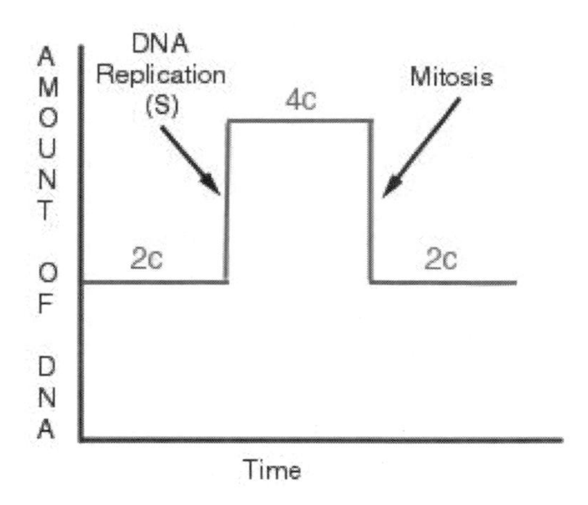

Draw a cell containing 1 pair of homologous chromosomes after it undergoes DNA replication (i.e. S phase) as seen in metaphase.

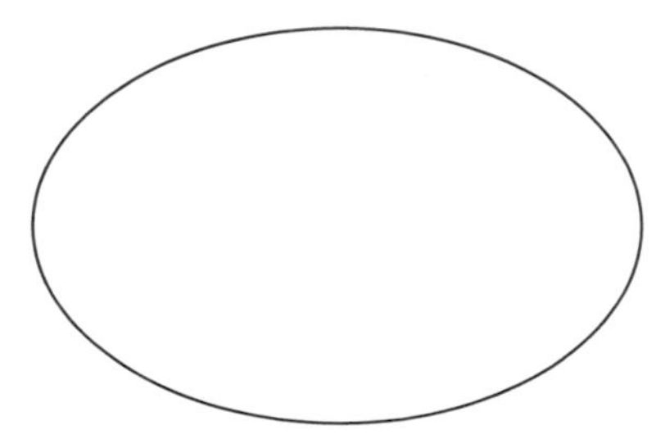

Suppose one homologue carries the a allele and the other homologue carries the A allele. Label each chromatid in your drawing.

Put each of the pictures below (containing two pairs of homologous chromosomes) in correct order and label with the appropriate phase. Note: homologous chromosomes do not have to be next to each other during mitosis.

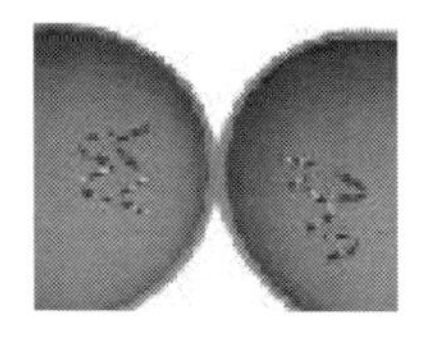 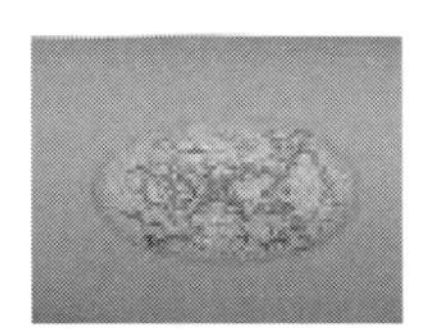 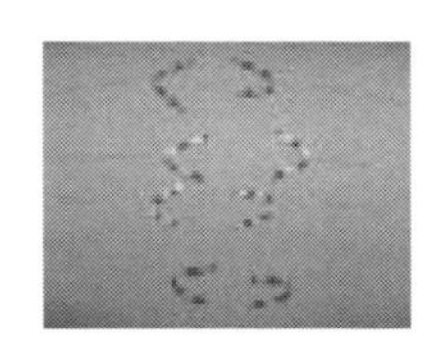 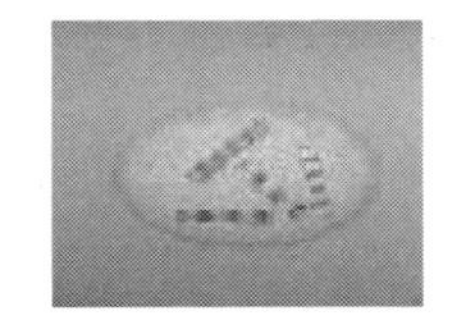 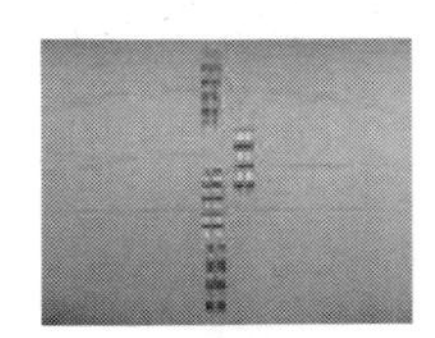

__________ __________ __________ __________ __________

Draw two daughter cells generated by a mitotic division with the appropriate homologues (labeled with A and a).

Problem 2

The results Mendel observed from his early crosses established the idea that alleles segregate. Unfortunately, Mendel couldn't figure out the biological mechanism behind this principle.

About 100 years ago, scientists realized that gametes (sex cells) were the result of a specialized cell division. This division process began with a cell that has two sets of chromosomes (a diploid cell) and ended with four cells with only one set of chromosomes (a haploid gamete). Today we know that the segregation of homologous chromosomes within this division process, meiosis, provides the mechanism for the segregation of alleles.

During sexual reproduction, two gametes (one from the mother, one from the father) combine in fertilization to form a diploid cell. A diploid fly has eight chromosomes. Without meiosis, how many chromosomes would the first generation progeny contain?

The purpose of meiosis is to convert one diploid cell into four haploid cells, each containing a single complete set of chromosomes. Meiosis can be divided into two cycles: Division I and Division II (or Meiosis I and Meiosis II). Two cells result from meiosis I. For a cell with a single pair of homologous chromosomes (labeled with A/a), draw the chromosomes found in the two cells formed by the first meiotic division. Then draw the four products of meiosis, with the appropriately labeled chromosome.

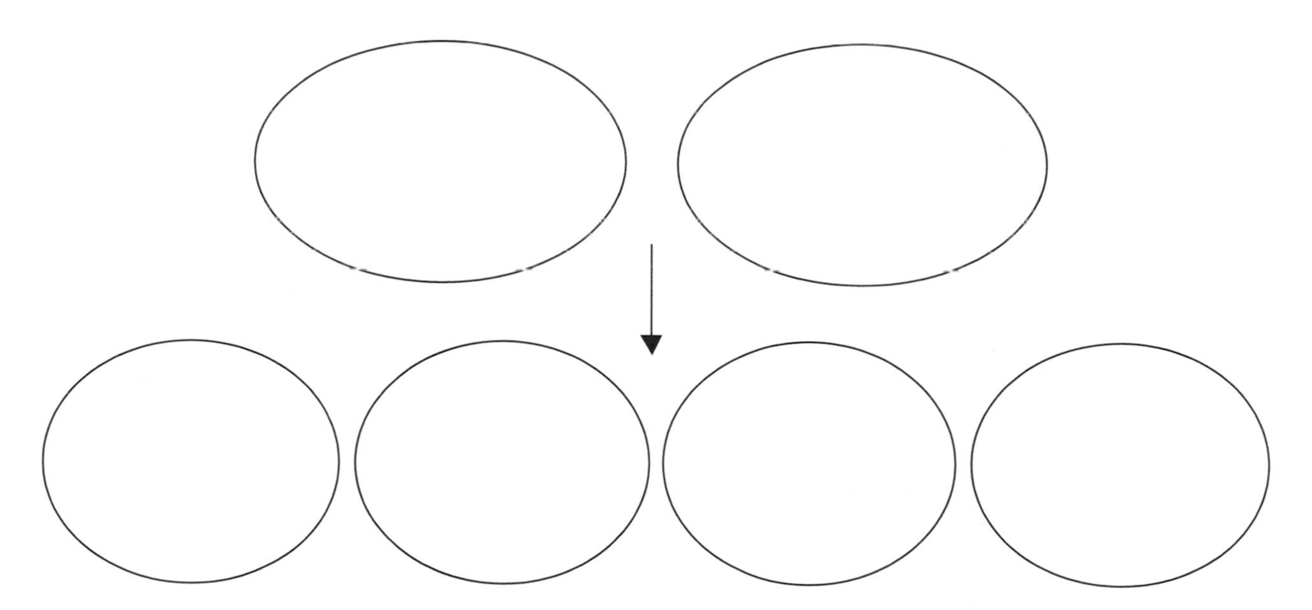

How many types of gametes with different alleles are formed in this example?

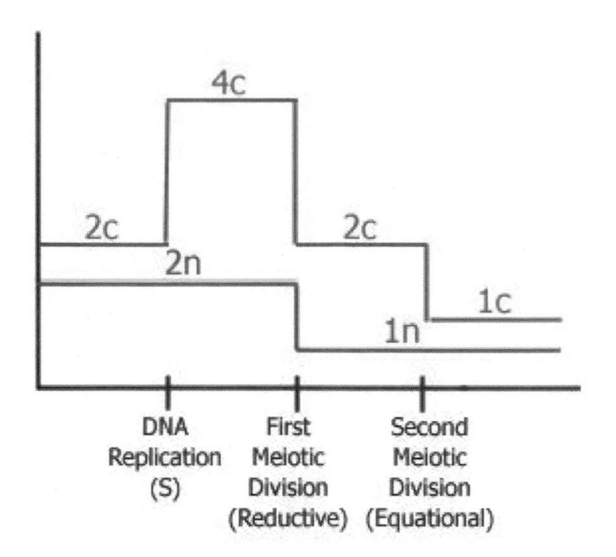

Regardless of whether there are 1 or 2 chromatids per chromosome, n indicates the number of chromosomes in a cell. Recall that c refers to the concentration of DNA in a cell.

vv

a

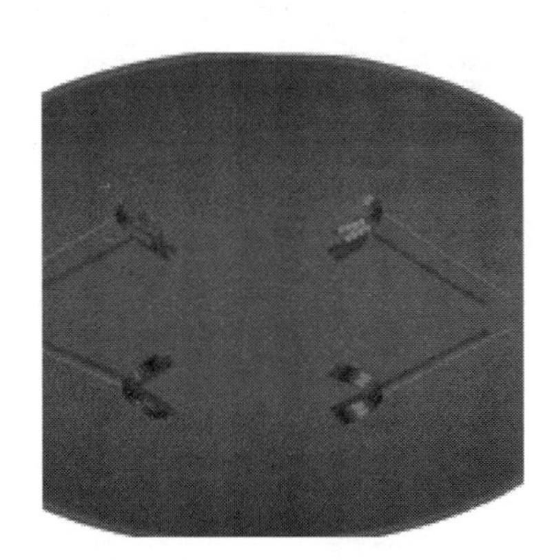

What phase of meiosis best describes the cell in figure a?

How many pairs of homologous chromosomes are there in this cell?

How many chromatids are present?

What is the value of c at this stage of meiosis?

b

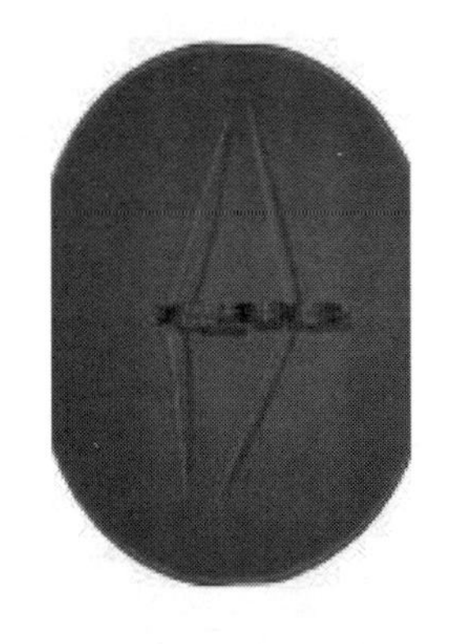

What phase of meiosis best describes the cell in figure b?

Does the cell shown here have 1n or 2n chromosomes?

Is the amount of DNA best described as c, 2c or 4c?

c

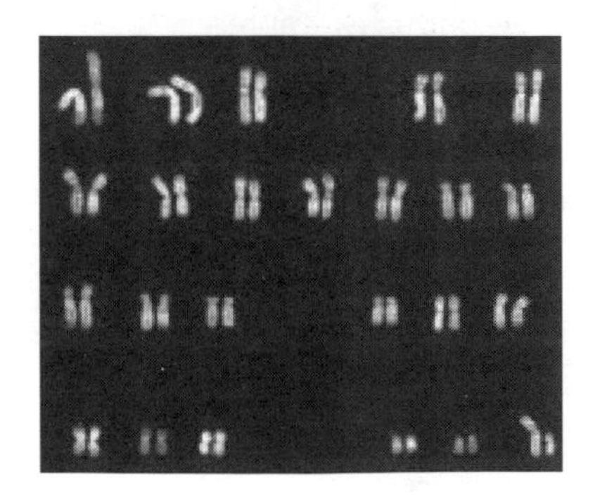

A karyotype (figure c) is the ordered visualization of a complete set of chromosomes from metaphase. Karyotypes can be used to determine the number of chromosomes a species has, as well as any abnormalities an individual chromosome might have. This is the karotype of a male gorilla. How many chromosomes does a gorilla have? How many chromosomes are found in a gorilla gamete?

Autosomes are the same in both males and females. Sex chromosomes (bottom right corner) differ according to sex (XX in females, XY in males). X and Y chromosomes behave as homologues in males (the X and Y chromosomes pair and segregate at meiosis I). How many chromosomally different gamete types does a male produce?

Problem 3

Through the analysis of dihybrid crosses, Mendel was able to deduce that the genes he was studying were assorting independently, giving rise to gametic ratios of 1:1:1:1. However, in 1865, the physical nature of this independent assortment was not understood. After the discovery of meiosis in the 1880's, scientists recognized that genes located on different chromosomes should assort independently. A physical basis for Mendel's hypothesis was now possible!

The genetic material must be duplicated (or replicated) prior to it's assortment. Draw two pairs of homologous chromosomes (labeled with A/a and B/b) in the cell below as it would appear after DNA replication (in prophase I).

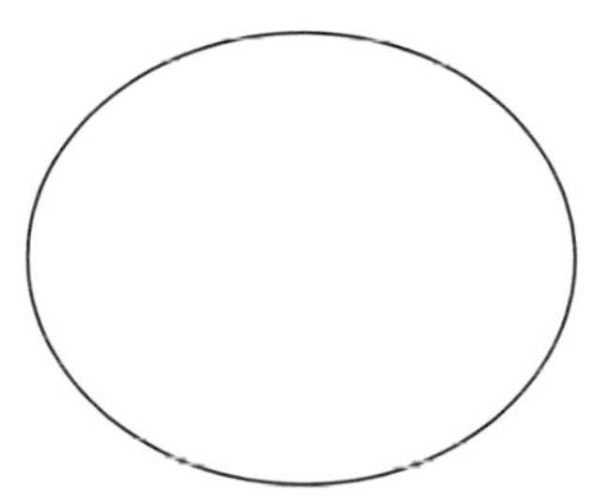

Two cells result from the first division of meiosis. Draw the chromosomes as they would appear in cells after meiosis I. Remember that there are two different equally probable ways for the chromosomes to assort (just draw one).

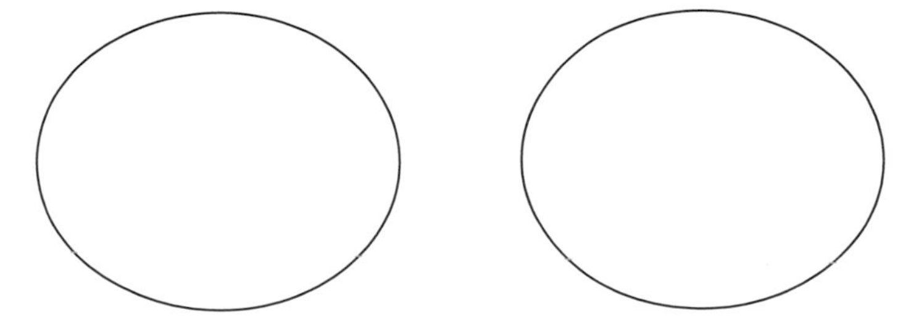

Write the possible gametes produced by a female with the genotype *AaBb*.

What are the possible gametes produced by a male with the genotype *AaBb?*

Notice that the gametes produced are identical to the meiotic products for an AaBb x AaBb cross. Recall that Punnett square accurately predicts the genotypic frequencies when the genes involved assort independently of one another. In further testing Mendel's law of independent assortment, you cross a *Aa Bb Dd* female mouse with a *aa bb dd* male. How many possible gamete types can the female produce?

Suppose instead of seeing the number of classes of mice you expected, you find only four. You find 30 *abd*, 33 *aBd*, 29 *AbD*, and 28 *ABD* mice. In order to explain this enigma, we will look at one possible arrangement of genes on the mother's chromosomes.

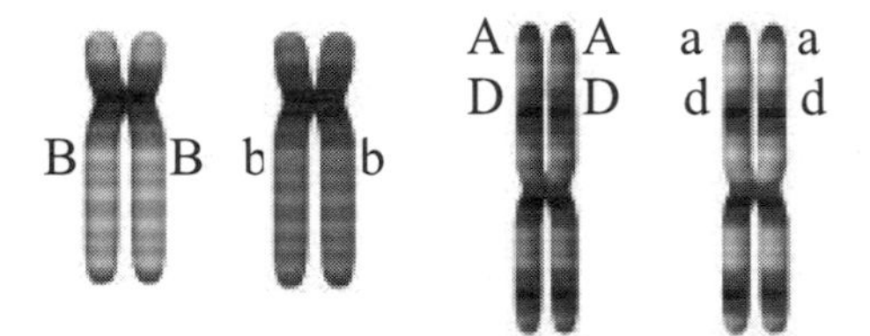

Two cells result from the first division of meiosis. Draw the chromosomes shown above to create the cells after meiosis I. Note that even though the two chromosomes are assorting randomly, the A and D alleles travel together since they are on the same chromosome.

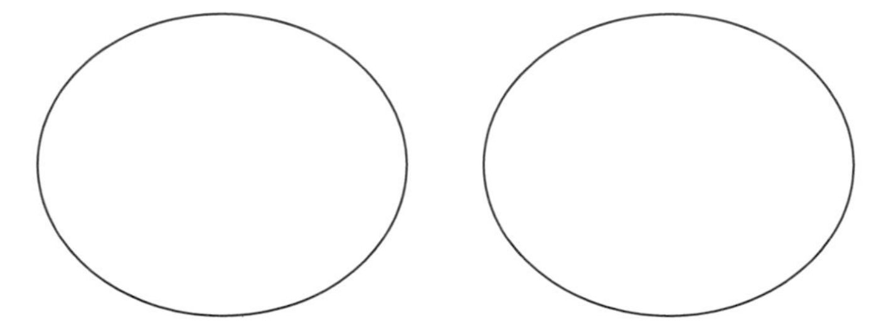

Completion of meiosis will produce four gamete types. What are the four possible genotypes (consider both possible assortments)?

This is an example of tightly linked genes on a chromosome where no crossing over can occur (see topic Linkage).

Problem 4

Problem 4 is a series of cartoons of cells at different stages of meiosis and mitosis and should be done on the CD-ROM.

X-Linked Inheritance
Problem 1

Is the pedigree below consistent with a dominant or a recessive trait? Assume the trait is rare.

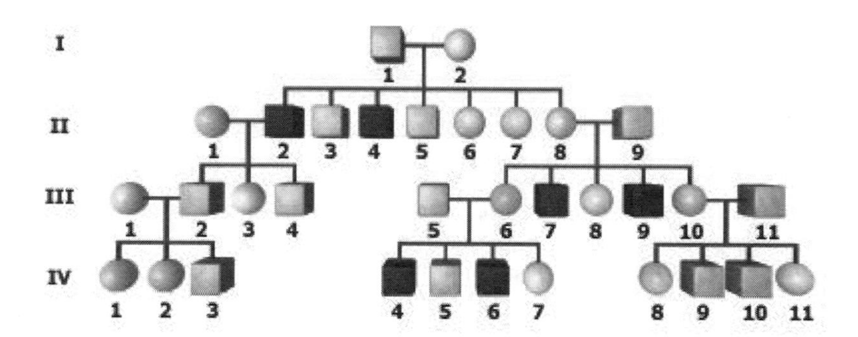

Is this pedigree consistent with X-linked or autosomal inheritance? Assume the trait is rare.

In the pedigree above, is there any evidence of father to son transmission of the trait?

What is the genotype of individual II-2? Write A or a for the X-linked alleles and Y for the Y chromosome.

What is the genotype of individual III-6? Write A or a to designate the X-linked dominant or recessive alleles.

Suppose in the pedigree above, individual II-8 was a male instead of a female and individual II-9 a female instead of a male. All other individuals are unchanged. Would this change the mode of inheritance deduced from this pedigree?

Is this pedigree still consistent with a recessive trait?

Can you tell whether the trait, in this hypothetical pedigree, is common or rare?

Now that the mode of inheritance is different, what is the genotype of individual II-2? Use A or a for the dominant and recessive alleles, respectively.

Problem 2

Hemophilia is a rare, recessive X-linked disease that usually affects only males. Consider the pedigree below of a family of normal parents with a son who has hemophilia.

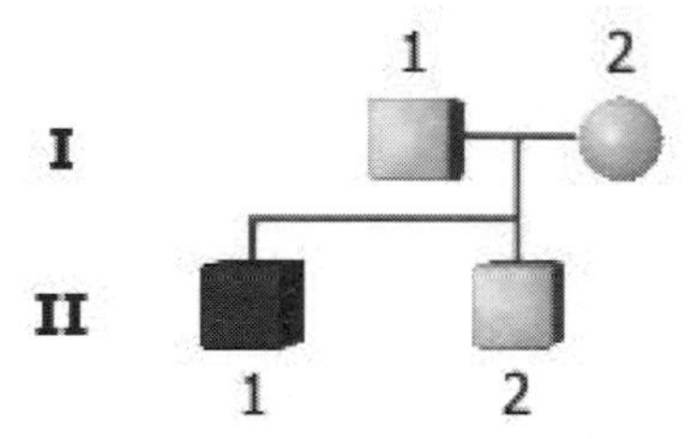

What is the father's genotype? Write H for X^H, h for X^h, or Y.

What is the mother's genotype? Write H for X^H and h for X^h.
They are going to have another child, whom they know is male (individual II-3). What is the chance that he will be affected?

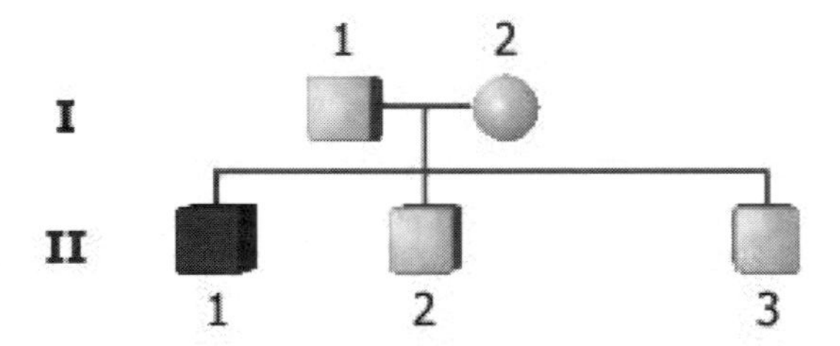

What is the chance that a daughter (individual II-5) will be a carrier?

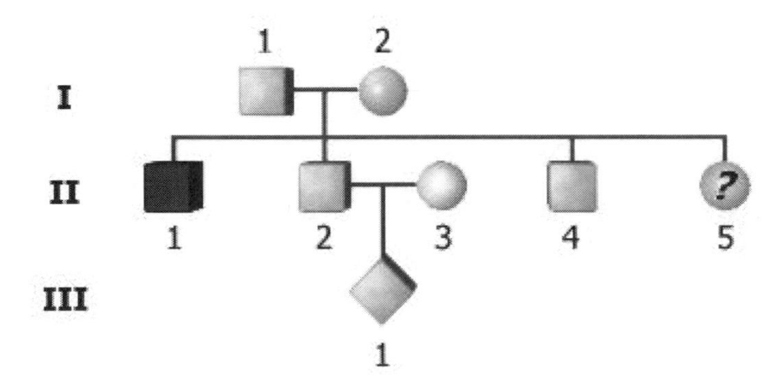

What is the probability that the child III-1 will be affected?

What is the probability that the child III-1 will be a carrier girl?

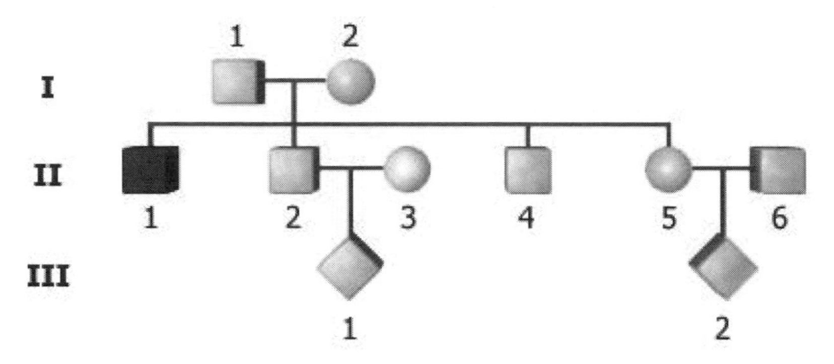

What is the probability that the child III-2 will be an affected boy?

Problem 3

The pedigree below belongs to a family with a rare trait known as vitamin D resistant rickets. Is this pedigree consistent with a dominant or recessive mode of inheritance?

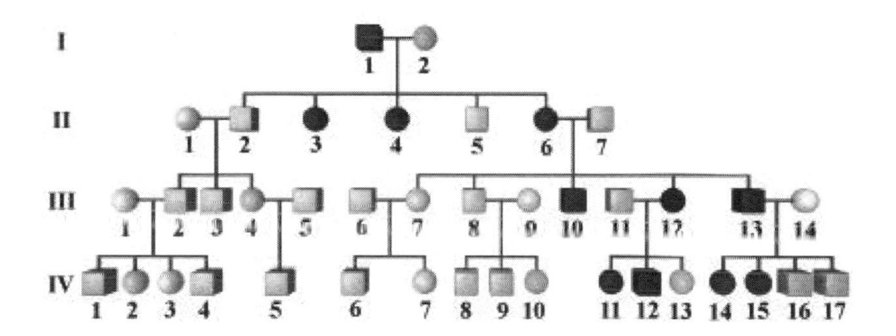

Is this pedigree consistent with an autosomal or an X-linked trait?

Assuming the trait is X-linked, what is II-6's genotype? Use A or a to designate the dominant or recessive X-linked alleles.

What is the genotype of individual II-5? Use A or a to designate the dominant or recessive X-linked alleles.

Suppose that III-14 has just found out she is going to have another girl. What is the probability that the child will be affected?

Individuals III-11 and III-12 are going to have another child but they don't know its sex. What is the probability they will have an affected son?

Problem 4

Red green colorblindness is a common X-linked recessive trait in humans that affects both males and females. Affected individuals are unable to distinguish red from green. Its prevalence accounts for the fact that you see some affected females as well as affected males.

Sickle cell anemia is an autosomal recessive disorder with a high incidence in the African American population (1/400). It is a structural hemoglobin abnormality that causes sickling of red blood cells with resulting complications.

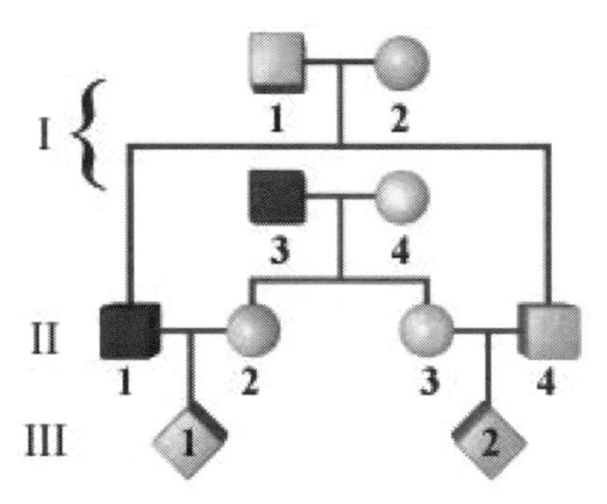

Consider this pedigree of two brothers marrying two sisters. All the individuals in generation II, namely II-1, II-2, II-3, and II-4 are carriers of the sickle cell allele. Individuals with filled blue squares are colorblind. Is there a greater chance that child III-1 will have sickle cell anemia than child III-2?

What is the chance that the child (III-1) will be colorblind and have sickle cell anemia?

What is the probability that child (III-2) will be colorblind and affected with sickle cell anemia?

If the child (III-2) from the second marriage is colorblind, what's the child's gender?

Problem 5

Nondisjunction is a rare event that occurs in meiosis when paired chromosomes or sister chromatids do not disjoin properly. When this occurs in meiosis I, both homologues end up in one daughter cell. When nondisjunction occurs in the meiosis II, one of the four meiotic cells ends up with both sister chromatids from one chromosome, and the other meiotic cell involved doesn't have any copies of that chromosome.

In humans, nondisjunction is generally lethal except when it involves chromosome 21 (leading to Down syndrome) or the sex chromosomes. In the following examples, nondisjunction of the sex chromosomes will be examined in conjunction with the X-linked gene that causes red green colorblindness. Affected individuals are unable to distinguish red color from green. In severely affected individuals, everything appears gray.

A man who is colorblind has a daughter with Turner syndrome who is also colorblind. You want to explain the origin of this daughter through nondisjunction in one parent.

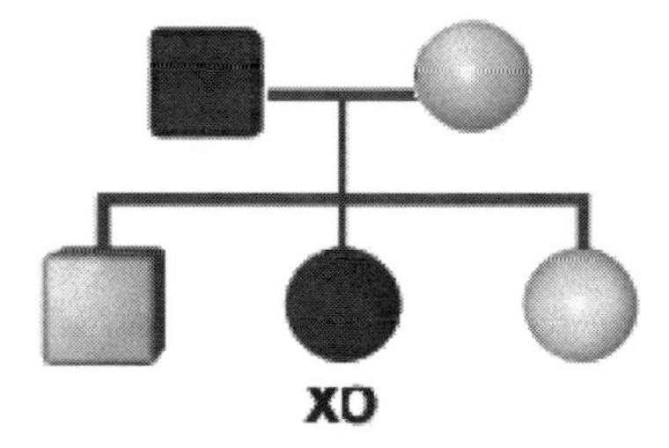

Assuming the mother is not a carrier of the colorblindness allele, use the genetic marker of colorblindness in this family to determine which parent had the nondisjunction event.

Can you tell at what stage of meiosis (meiosis I or meiosis II) nondisjunction occurred?

A woman who is colorblind has a son with Klinefelter (XXY) syndrome who is not colorblind. You want to explain the origin of this son through nondisjunction in one parent. Start by assigning a genotype to each individual.

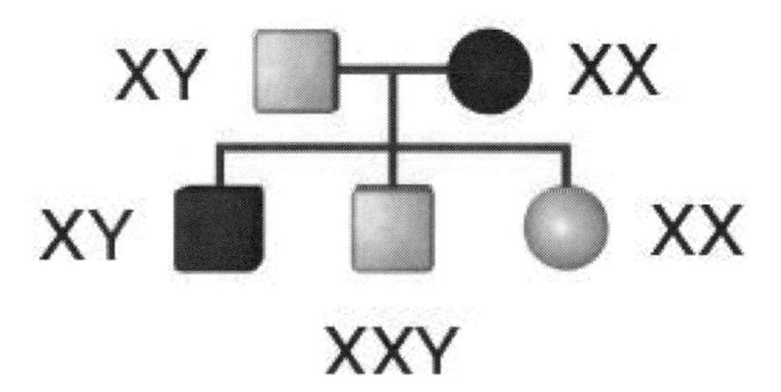

Can you use the genetic marker of colorblindness in this family to determine which parent had the nondisjunction event? Indicate that parent in the pedigree above.

Can you determine whether the nondisjunction event occurred in meiosis I or meiosis II of the parent's gametic line?

In the Drosophila fruit fly, the gene for white eyes is located on the X-chromosome. The white-eyed allele is recessive to the wildtype. In crosses between white-eyed females and wildtype males almost all (regular) daughters have red eyes, except for about 1/2000 (0.05%) exceptional white-eyed daughters. Almost all (regular) sons have white eyes except for about 1/2000 exceptional red eyed sons that are sterile.

Upon inspection of the flies' karyotypes, the white-eyed exceptional daughters were found to carry XXY. (Regular females are XX and males are XY.) Does this finding indicate that the Y chromosome determines sex in fruit flies?

Indicate the correct alleles of the exceptional females, one allele at a time. Follow the Drosophila nomenclature rules (see Fly Lab below) and choose between w and W for the white-eyed allele, and between w+ and W+ for the wildtype allele.

When the exceptional red eyed sons are inspected, they are found to be XO, having a single X chromosome. Does this fact agree with the conclusion that the presence of Y does not determine sex in the Drosophila fruit flies?

Do these unusual findings of white-eyed exceptional daughters and red-eyed exceptional sons represent nondisjunction in the Drosophila father or Drosophila mother?

Can we tell whether the nondisjunction occurred in the first meiotic division or in the second meiotic division?

Fly Lab

Welcome to the fly lab! The following problems allow you to play the role of a geneticist working with the common fruit fly, *Drosophila melanogaster*. Since Drosophila nomenclature may be confusing at first, here is a brief review:

Genes are named after the mutant phenotype in Drosophila. Therefore, if the mutant gene results in the lack of eye formation, the gene could be named "eyeless." (Note this differs from the Mendelian designations used for peas, for example, where the gene is typically named after the dominant trait.)

When allele symbols are assigned, lower case is used if the mutant allele is recessive (for example *ro* for rough eyes). Capitalizing the first letter indicates that the mutant allele is inherited as a dominant trait (for example *N* for notched wings).

Wildtype alleles are designated with a superscript + (eg. ro^+ or N^+). In the following problems simply indicate the + after the allele symbol (i.e. *ro*+ or *N*+).

The problems below are set up as simulations on the CD-ROM. Here, the results are provided.

Problem 1

In Drosophila, the brown mutant is characterized by a brown eye color compared with the brick red, wildtype color. A wildtype fly is crossed with a brown-eyed fly to produce the F1 generation and then the F1 flies are crossed to produce the F2 generation.

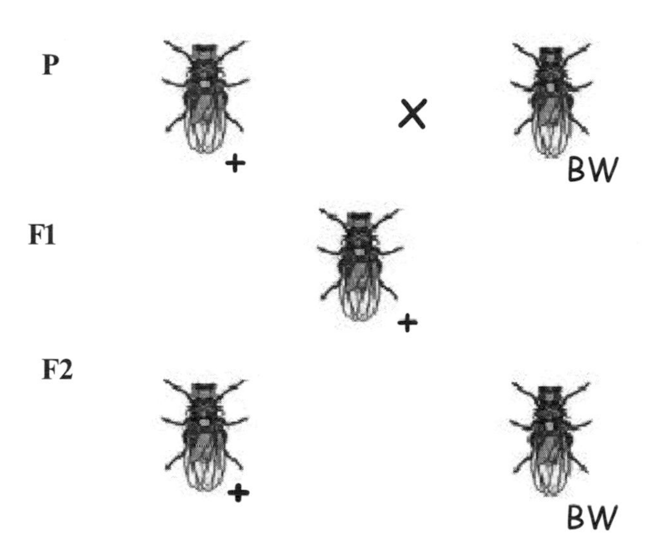

Is the brown mutation dominant or recessive?

Using the letters BW and proper Drosophila nomenclature (bw for recessive and Bw for dominant), indicate the proper mutant allele designation below.

What is the genotype of each of the flies above?

Problem 2

In Drosophila, the lobed mutation is characterized by smaller eyes compared to the wildtype. A wildtype fly is crossed with a lobed fly to produce the F1 generation (all lobed). Then the F1 flies are crossed with each other to produce the F2 generation (768 lobed and 259 wildtype).

Is the lobed mutation dominant or recessive?

How would you indicate the mutant allele using the correct Drosophila nomenclature?

What is the genotype of each of the parental, F1 and F2 flies?

What fraction of the mutant F2 flies are homozygous?

Problem 3

In Drosophila, the white mutant is characterized by white eyes compared to the brick red, wildtype color. A wildtype female fly is crossed with a white-eyed male to produce 974 wildtype F1 flies. At this point what can you conclude about the mutation (is it dominant or recessive)?

The reciprocal cross is then performed: a wildtype male is mated with a white-eyed female to produce 436 white-eyed males and 421 wildtype females.

What can you now conclude about the mode of inheritance (autosomal or X-linked)?

Now go back to each of the crosses above and write the genotype of all the flies.

Problem 4

In Drosophila, the bar mutant is characterized by eyes that are restricted to a narrow, vertical bar. When a bar female is mated to a wildtype male, all the F1 flies are bar. However, when a bar male is mated to wildtype female, 857 bar females and 905 wildtype males are observed.

What is the mode of inheritance of the bar mutant?

What is the genotype of each of the flies in the two crosses above?

Problem 5

In Drosophila, the ebony mutant is characterized by a ebony body color and purple is characterized by purple eyes. Mating an ebony purple female with a wildtype male yields all wildtype progeny. The reciprocal cross gives the same results.

What is the mode of inheritance for the ebony mutation?

What is the mode of inheritance for the purple mutation?

What is the genotype of the F1 flies?

Mating the F1 flies together yields 226 wildtype, 74 ebony, 78 purple and 25 ebony purple flies. What is the ratio of progeny for each of the phenotypic classes?

Which F2 fly should you use for a testcross of the F1 flies?

How many different phenotypic classes, and in what ratios, do you expect from this cross?

Problem 6

In Drosophila, the sable mutant is characterized by a sable body color and dumpy is characterized by shorter, oblique wings. In a cross between a sable, dumpy female and a wildtype male, all the female progeny are wildtype and the male progeny are sable. When the F1 siblings are mated, the F2 consists of 338 wildtype, 336 sable, 114 dumpy and 110 sable, dumpy (both male and female).

What is the mode of inheritance of the sable mutant?

What is the mode of inheritance of the dumpy mutation?

In order to understand the unusual ratios and the lack of apparent linkage to sex of the sable phenotype in the F2, assign genotypes to the parental and F1 generations. Write the genotypes above, using s or s+ or Y to indicate sable alleles and dp or dp+ to indicate dumpy alleles. Predict the proportion of each phenotype you would expect in the F2.

Genotype/Phenotype

Goals for Genotype/Phenotype:

1. Understand the following phenomena that lead to variations on Mendelian phenotypic ratios.
   - Incomplete dominance
   - Codominance
   - Epistasis
   - Homozygous lethality
2. Recognize combinations of 9:3:3:1 phenotypic ratios, where the phenotype comes from two genes and involves epistasis.
3. Distinguish from phenotypic ratios whether multiple genes or a single gene with multiple alleles are involved in determining the phenotypes.

Problem 1

Gardeners at the Japanese Botanical Garden discovered that after planting only red and ivory snapdragons some plants with pink flowers appeared among the progeny. The gardeners decided to experiment with the snapdragon flowers and carried out a number of additional crosses. In this diagram, the parents are shown along the margins with progeny types inside the boxes.

Parents	Red	Ivory	Pink
Red	Red	Pink	Red, Pink
Ivory	Pink	Ivory	Ivory, Pink
Pink	Red, Pink	Pink, Ivory	Red, Ivory, Pink

Which of the parents are homozygous?

Which of the parents are heterozygous?

By crossing the PINK plants we should be able to distinguish whether their color is caused by one or more gene differences between the red and ivory parents. Take a moment to predict what offspring you expect for one gene versus two genes.

From the original results, the PINK X PINK cross yielded three phenotypes among the progeny. The numbers of each of the phenotypes are listed below.

F2: 261 red
489 pink
243 ivory

What is the ratio suggested by these results?

How many genes differ between the RED and IVORY parents in determining flower color?

Assume the gene differing between the RED and IVORY parents has two alleles, *P1*, associated with the presence of red pigment and *P2*, associated with the absence of red pigment. What are the genotypes of the different progeny types in the F2 above?

Which of the following concepts best explains the observed results of the F1 and F2 progeny: incomplete dominance, codominance, P1 dominant, P2 dominant, multiple alleles or multiple genes?

Problem 2

The tools we use to infer genotypes are phenotypes and the results of crosses. A powerful advance is the ability to look at phenotypes that are closer to gene activity. Here we describe an example using gel electrophoresis of proteins.

Proteins can be separated based on size and/or charge using electrophoresis through a gel matrix. Migration distance through the gel serves as a phenotypic marker that could help determine an individual's genotype. Such is the case with the normal and the sickle cell hemoglobin molecules. With sickle cell, heterozygous individuals produce both normal and sickle cell hemoglobin molecules. When the normal and the abnormal hemoglobin molecules are run through a gel, they migrate at different rates and can be visually separated.

Part a. The family below has a history of sickle cell anemia. The hemoglobin electrophoresis pattern for each child is shown in the lanc below that child.

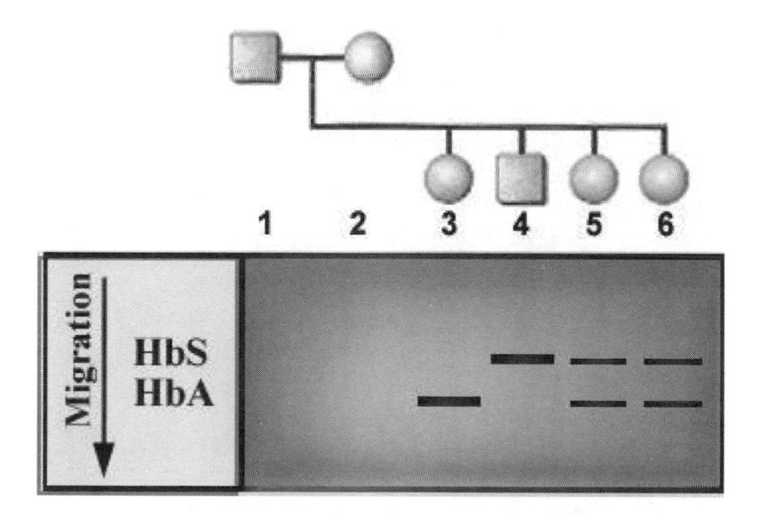

Which individuals in this family are homozygous for the sickle cell allele?

Which individuals from this family are heterozygous?

Imagine that this family is one out of a large number of families with heterozygous parents tested for their hemoglobin structure. Predict the ratios of children expected to be homozygous for HbA, homozygous for HbS and heterozygous.

Which of the following concepts can best explain the expected phenotypic ratio: HbA dominant, HbS dominant, Incomplete dominance or codominance?

Part b. Gel electrophoresis can be used to screen individuals for the HbS allele.

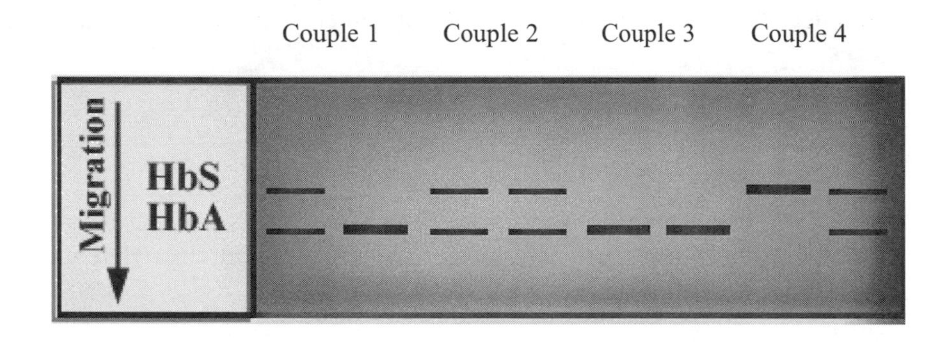

Which of the couples above are at risk of having an affected child?

What is the probability that couple 2 will have a child with sickle cell anemia?

Part c. Use the Southern blot below to determine which of the three males (4, 5, or 6) could be the children's father.

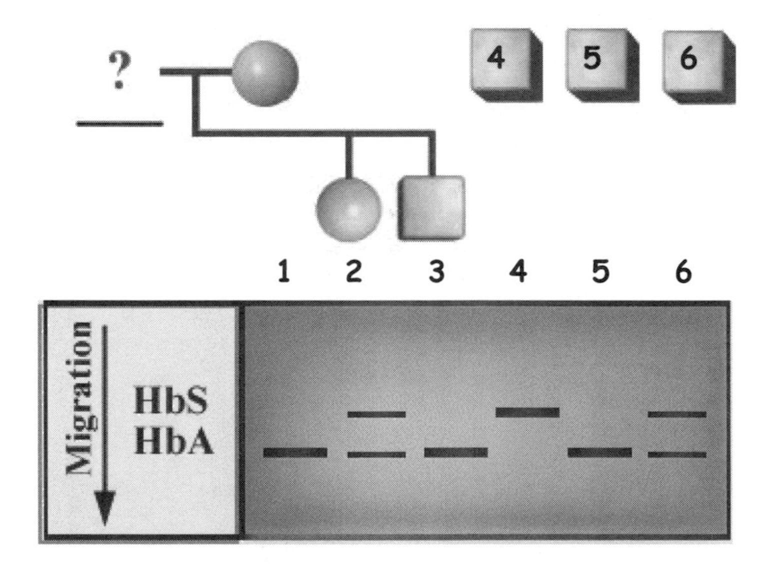

If this couple has another child, what is the chance the child will be anemic?

Problem 3

Karl Landsteiner was an Austrian-American physician who discovered that human blood differed in the capacity of serum to agglutinate red blood cells. By 1902, he and his group divided human blood into the groups A, B, AB, and O. Landsteiner concluded that two genes, A and B, control the ABO blood system he discovered. He proposed that each gene had two alleles, the presence and the absence of that allele.

Genotype	Phenotype
A- bb	A
aa B-	B
A- B-	AB
aa bb	O

Since you have been volunteering in Labor and Delivery for quite some time, you decide to compare the blood types you would expect using Landsteiner's two-gene hypothesis to the blood types you have observed. What genotype do you expect the children of two type O parents will have?

What is the expected phenotype of their children?

From your observations, 500 O x O parents have 763 type O children, whereas no type A, type B or type AB children are observed. Is this consistent with the two-gene hypothesis?

One day you realize that in all 503 O x AB couples you have never seen any AB or O children. You have observed 600 type A and 650 type B children. Is this what you would predict based upon Landsteiner's hypothesis?

*Additional related questions are on the CD-ROM.

Problem 4

Suppose you are studying a novel bird species which displays a variation in feathers (blue, green, teal and purple). Starting with pure breeding males and females from each phenotypic class, you perform the crosses diagrammed below.

Parents	F1	F2
Teal x green	Teal	¾ teal, ¼ green
Green x blue	Green	¾ green, ¼ blue
Teal x purple	Teal	¾ teal, ¼ purple
Green x purple	Green	¾ green, ¼ purple
Blue x purple	Purple	¾ purple, ¼ blue

Based on the data shown above, is feather color in this novel species segregating as if it were associated with multiple genes or multiple alleles?

Using the data shown above, which allele is dominant blue or green?

Blue or purple?

Green or purple?

Green or teal?

What is the order of alleles corresponding to increasing dominance?

Cross	Parental Phenotypes	Phenotypes of Progeny			
		Blue	Green	Purple	Teal
1	blue x green	0	4	4	0
2	green x purple	0	3	3	0
3	teal x blue	0	4	0	4
4	teal x purple	0	4	0	3
5	green x green	0	6	2	0

For each of the crosses shown above, deduce the parental genotypes where f represents the feather gene and the following superscript designations represent the different alleles:

b - blue; g - green; p - purple; t – teal

*Assume homozygosity unless otherwise indicated.

Problem 5

A geneticist discovered two pure breeding lines of ducks. One line had white eyes and quacked with a "quack-quack". The other line had orange eyes and had a deeper quack, "rock-rock". In order to determine the mode of inheritance of these characteristics, she mated the two types of ducks and found that all F1 ducks had yellow eyes, and uttered quack-quack. When the F1 ducks were interbred, the F2 ducks were found in the following ratios:

24 yellow eyed, quack-quack
12 white eyed, quack-quack
12 orange eyed, quack-quack
6 yellow eyed, rock-rock
3 white eyed, rock-rock
3 orange eyed, rock-rock
2 yellow eyed, squawk
1 white eyed, squawk
1 orange eyed, squawk

How many genes are involved in the inheritance of eye color?

P orange-eyed x white-eyed

F1 yellow-eyed

F2
2 yellow-eyed
1 orange-eyed
1 white-eyed

Use A1/A2, B1/B2, etc. to designate eye color alleles, assign genotypes to the individuals in the cross described above.

How many genes are involved in the inheritance of quacking?

P		quack-quack x rock-rock
F1		quack-quack
F2	12	quack-quack
	3	rock-rock
	1	squawk

Use B/b, C/c, etc. to designate quacking phenotype, assign genotypes to the individuals in the cross described above.

Problem 6

Recall from problem 4 that blood types are classified by their surface antigens. Type A blood has antigen A on its surface, type B has antigen B, type AB has both antigen A and antigen B, and type O has neither antigen on its surface.

Ellen and Carl have just had a baby boy. Ellen's blood type is B, Carl's is AB and the baby's is O. Having a good knowledge of blood typing you realize that something is not quite right with this story. You happen to know that Ellen's parents' blood types are B and O. From this, what is Ellen's genotype?

What is Carl's genotype?

Does it appear that Ellen and Carl can have a child with O blood?

Ellen's ex-boyfriend, Mark, has type O blood. Could Mark be the baby's father?

Ellen insists that Carl is the father, so you look into their family history (you may notice that Ellen and Carl are cousins). The results are seen in the pedigree below. Which parents have phenotype(s) that are incompatible with the blood types of their children?

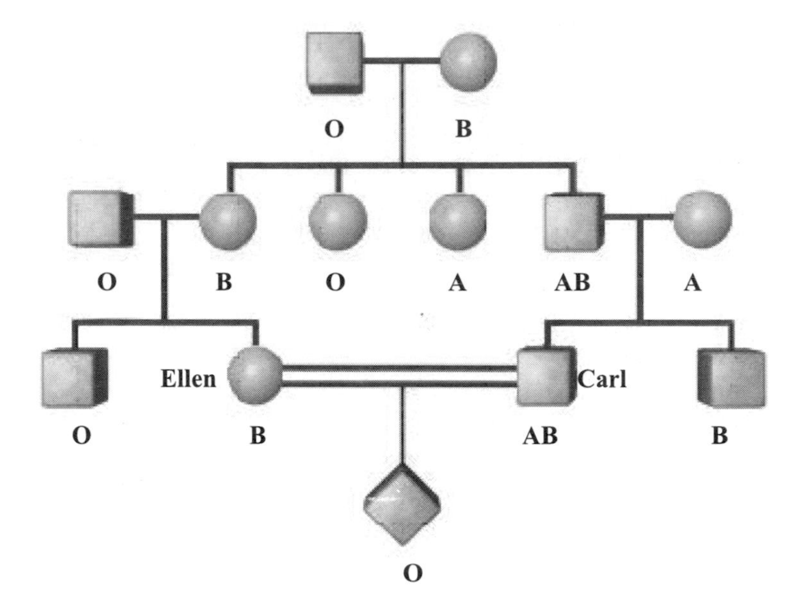

One of your friends suggest that this may be an example of lack of penetrance, i.e. the phenotype does not reflect the genotype. However, since Ellen and Carl share a grandfather who also has a suspicious O phenotype, you wonder if it's possible that they both inherited a recessive allele that is epistatic to the ABO blood antigens.

Upon further research you find there is such a rare recessive mutation, *h*, that is epistatic to the ABO system gene. Individuals who are homozygous for *h* cannot synthesize A or B antigens, so they have an O phenotype, referred to as the Bombay phenotype.

Assign genotypes for the H gene assuming this is the reason for the unusual phenotypes (use *H/h*). With this information, determine the genotype for the ABO locus for individual I-1.

Does it now appear that Carl could be the father?

Does this information conclusively prove that Carl is the father?

In the hope of solving the paternity issue, you decide to run a Southern Blot, probing for the alleles of the H gene.

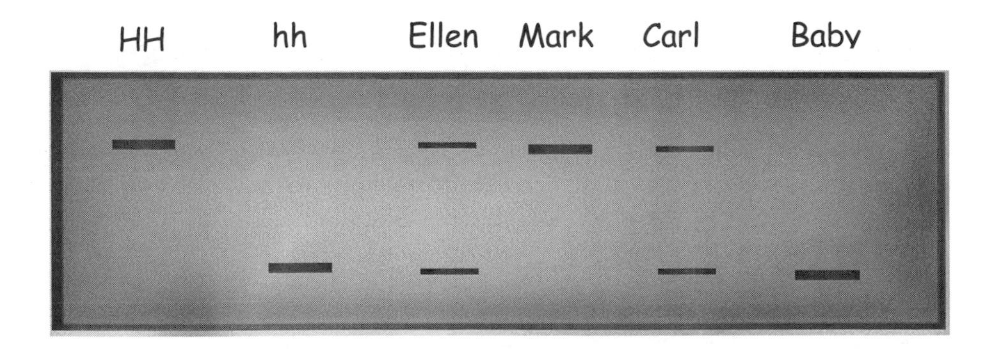

With this information, can you definitively say who is the baby's father?

Problem 7

Carolyn and Jeff are both cat-lovers and neighbors in a local apartment complex. Recently, Carolyn's cat, Grace, escaped from her apartment and was seen mating with Jeff's ferocious feline, Chuck. Although Carolyn and Jeff were initially upset with the scandalous behavior of their pets, they felt reassured that Grace and Chuck would produce a beautiful and profitable litter of kittens. Weeks later, Carolyn and Jeff discovered the litter of kittens and were surprised to find one cat with curled ears.

As their close friend and local genetics expert, they turn to you to provide a genetic explanation for this strange occurrence. At this point, can you determine whether the curled ear cat occurred as a result of a spontaneous dominant mutation or whether both parents were heterozygous for a recessive mutant allele?

In order to determine whether the curled-ear mutation is dominant or recessive to the normal condition, you mate the curled ear cat with an unrelated normal cat. From this mating, *2 curled-ear cats and 2 normal cats* are produced. Based on these results, is the curled ear mutant allele dominant or recessive to the wildtype allele?

The allele responsible for curled ears in cats is located at the Ear locus. Using the allele symbols c and c+, assign genotypes to the cats in the cross described above. Be sure to follow the format shown below when assigning genotypes:

Homozygous Individuals: cc or c+c+
Heterozygous Individuals: cc+ or c+c

What ratio of curled ear cats to normal cats do you expect from the mating of two heterozygous curled ear cats?

After performing the mating between two heterozygous curled ear cats, you wait several weeks and examine the litter of kittens. The mating produced 4 curled ear cats and two normal cats. From these results, can you be certain about the mode of inheritance of curled ears?

What results do you expect for a mating between a homozygous curled ear cat and a normal cat?

What results do you expect for a mating between a heterozygous curled ear cat and a normal cat?

You decide to perform 170 matings between curled-eared cats to determine whether curled ears are inherited in a simple Mendelian manner. You obtain 1020 kittens from your 170 matings between heterozygous curled ear cats. If curled ears are inherited according to our predicted 3 to 1 ratio, how many curled ear cats do you expect to see out of the 1020 kittens?

You only observe 677 curled ear cats and 343 normal cats from the 170 matings. After re-counting the kittens several times, you are certain that the number of curled ear cats is accurate. What is our observed ratio of curled ear cats to normal ear cats?

What is the most likely genetic explanation for the results we have gathered?

Linkage

Goals for Linkage Analysis:

1. Recognize the difference between linkage and independent assortment in dihybrid crosses.
2. Relate parental chromosome input to linkage phase to calculate recombination frequencies.
3. Be able to make maps from recombination frequencies.
4. Use three factor crosses to distinguish order and distances between genes.

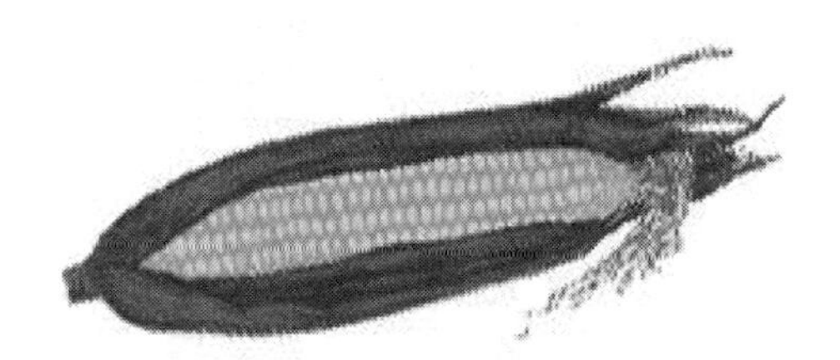

Problem 1

Consider two corn mutants: dwarf, and glossy. Dwarf (gene symbol *d*) is a recessive trait characterized by short, compact plants. Glossy (gene symbol *gl*) is also recessive and is characterized by a bright leaf surface. F1 progeny from a cross of pure breeding parents, were back crossed to the recessive parent. The results of this cross are shown below.

F2:		
	286	wildtype
	89	glossy
	97	dwarf
	277	glossy dwarf

Sincc the ratio of phenotypic classes is not the expected 1:1:1:1 for a test cross, what concept best explains the observed phenotypic ratio?

What phenomenon explains the four phenotypic classes of unequal ratios instead of two phenotypic classes as predicted by the tight linkage?

Complete the genotype of each F2 progeny class. Which phenotypic classes carry the recombinant genotypes?

What approximate percentage of progeny is descended from distinguishable recombinant gametes?

What is the map distance between dwarf and glossy determined from these numbers?

Using the known map distance between glossy and dwarf determined above, what is the expected number of each F2 phenotypic class out of a total of 1000 F2 progeny?

Problem 2

In Drosophila, the forked phenotype is characterized by short bristles with split ends. The scalloped phenotype is characterized by scalloped wings at the margins and thicker wing veins. Both genes are X-linked and are marked with recessive mutant alleles. In the cross below, an F1 is generated by mating a wildtype female with a scalloped, forked male to produce all wildtype progeny. The females are then mated to their fathers (a test cross) to generate an F2.

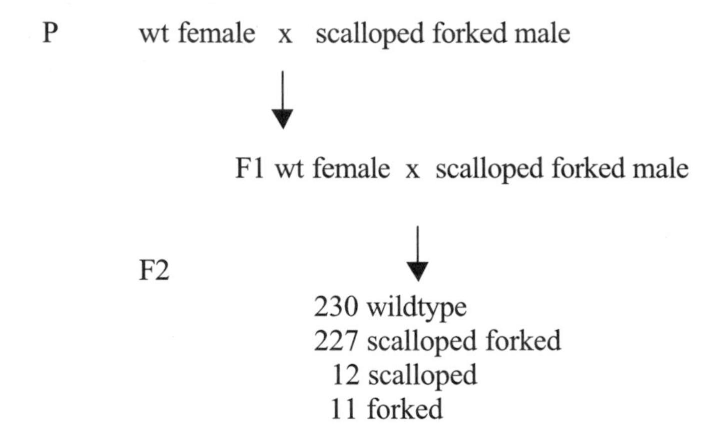

What concept best explains the observed phenotypic ratio of the F2 progeny?

Which of the phenotypes belongs to F2 progeny that that are descended from distinguishable crossover bearing (recombinant) gametes?

What approximate fraction of progeny are descended from distinguishable crossover bearing gametes?

What is the map distance between forked and scalloped?

Problem 3

The Drosophila forked phenotype is X-linked recessive (as we saw in Problem 2) and is characterized by short bristles with split ends. The miniature phenotype, also X-linked recessive, is characterized by reduced wing size.

A miniature female is crossed with a forked male. The F1 progeny consists of wildtype females and miniature males. These are then mated to yield the following F2:

510 miniature females	418 miniature males
490 wildtype females	412 forked males
	87 miniature forked males
	83 wildtype males

What is the approximate distance in map units (mu) between forked and miniature that you calculate from this cross?

When a wildtype female is crossed with a miniature forked male, and the wildtype F1 females are testcrossed, the F2 are as shown below:

84 miniature
86 forked
417 miniature forked
413 wildtype

Is the distance you find in mu the same in this cross as the distance you found for the markers in trans?

In problem 2 you found that the distance between the scalloped gene and the forked gene is 5 mu. In this problem you found that the distance between miniature and forked is 17 mu. Is this information sufficient to find the gene order of the three genes on the X chromosome?

When a wildtype female is crossed with a miniature scalloped male, all the progeny are wildtype. A testcross of the heterozygous females yields the following F2:

51 miniature
45 scalloped
354 miniature scalloped
350 wildtype

What is the approximate map unit (mu) distance between miniature and scalloped that you calculated from this cross?

Now that you know the distances between each pair of genes, construct a map of the three genes.

Problem 4

In Drosophila, the spineless mutant is characterized by shortened bristles compared to the longer bristles of the wildtype. The radius incomplete mutant is characterized by an incomplete wing vein pattern. Both genes are autosomal and are marked by recessive mutant alleles.

A wildtype female is mated with a spineless, incomplete male. Then, an F1 wildtype female is crossed to the parental male to generate the following F2:

449 wildtype
452 spineless incomplete
52 spineless
48 incomplete

In this cross you did not obtain the expected 1:1:1:1 ratio expected for a test cross of unlinked genes. This implies that the genes are linked. Use these data to calculate the distance between spineless and incomplete.

A wildtype male is mated with a spineless, incomplete female. Then, the F1 wildtype male is mated with the parental female. The following F2 progeny are observed:

361 wildtype flies
357 spineless incomplete flies

Note that very different results are observed in this F2 compared to the first cross. To help explain these unusual results, let's first assign genotypes to the F1 male and tester female.

Write the genotypes of the F1 flies in the cross above. Use the symbols *sp, sp+* for spineless and *ri or ri+* for radius incomplete. Indicate linkage by writing the two linked alleles on one side of a / (e.g. *a+b+/ab*).

After examination of these genotypes, does it make sense that these two genes are on the same chromosome?

Geneticists made a novel discovery when working with *Drosophila melanogaster.* Scientists found that male flies do <u>not</u> undergo recombination. Therefore, test cross of the F1 male yields only two gamete types. The distance between genes cannot be measured using F1 males. What gametes are produced in the F1 male fly?

The consequence of no recombination in males is that crosses to map linked genes must use F1 females as the dihybrid parent. This is true only in *Drosophila melanogaster*. In other species there is frequently a difference in recombination between the sexes, but it is not usually 0 in males.

Problem 5

In Drosophila, the X-linked genes singed (sn), characterized by bent bristles, miniature (m), reduced wing size, and tan (t), a tan body color, are marked with recessive alleles. In this problem you will use three-factor crosses to determine the gene order and distance between these markers. (Mating the F1 flies is essentially a test cross, allowing one to analyze all of the F2 flies directly).

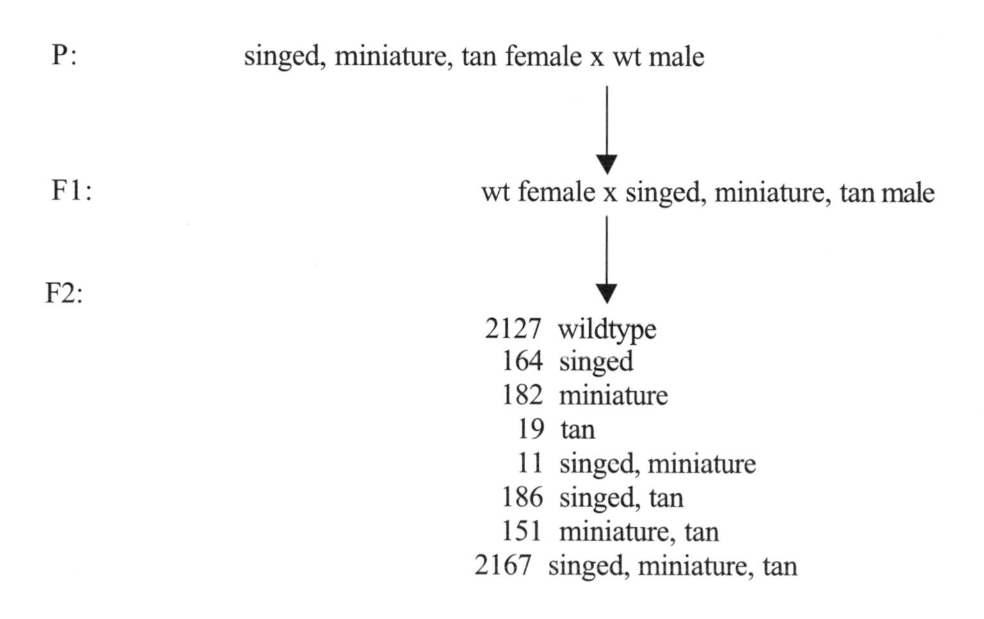

How many gamete types do you expect the F1 female to produce?

Which two classes of gamete types are the produced most often by the F1 female? (This is reflected in the phenotypic classes of the progeny.) These are the parental types.

Which of the reciprocal gamete types are the produced least often in the F1 female? (This is reflected in the phenotypic classes of the progeny.) These are the double crossover types.

Compare the double crossover gametes with the parental gametes to determine which gene is in the middle. Write the correct gene order below.

Using your data, determine the distance between the singed gene and the tan gene, and the distance between the tan gene and the miniature gene.

Problem 6

Chromosome 13 of the mouse carries the locus for flexed tail with the alleles *f* and *f+* and the locus for extra toes with the alleles *Et* and *Et+*. The flexed tail mutant is a recessive trait while the extra toes mutant is dominant. The next exercises will use 24 map units as the known distance between *Et* and *f* to predict the expected number of F2 progeny from crosses.

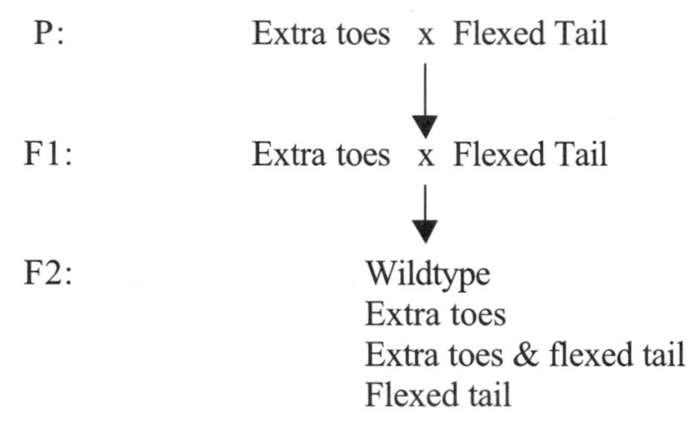

Find the genotype of each mouse above. Both parental mice are from pure breeding stocks. Use *Et* and *Et+* for the extra toes gene, and *f* or *f+* for the flexed tail gene.

Which F2 progeny represent recombinants?

The distance between *Et* and *f* is 24 mu. From a total of a 1000 F2 mice obtained from crosses such as this, how many are expected for each phenotypic class? (Start with the number of wildtype progeny.)

Wildtype
Extra toes
Extra toes & flexed tail
Flexed tail

Let's now try to find the expected progeny for a three point cross. Chromosome 13 of mouse also carries the locus for satin fur texture with the alleles *sa* and *sa+*. The satin fur mutant is a recessive trait. Use the following map unit distances to map sa: sa - Et: 4 mu, sa - f: 20 mu. Draw a map of the three markers.

Use this map to determine the number of predicted progeny of each phenotypic class shown below with parents of genotypes *Et f/Et f* and *sa/sa.* The F2 progeny classes from these crosses are as follows:

Wildtype
Flexed tail, satin with extra toes
Flexed tail with extra toes
Satin with extra toes
Flexed tail, satin
Extra toes
Flexed tail
Satin

Bacterial Genetics

Goals for Bacterial Genetics:

1. Be familiar with the mechanism of conjugation and transduction as methods of gene transfer.
2. Determine genotype from ability to grow on different media.
3. Determine type of media needed for selection of exconjugants.
4. Be familiar with replica plating and interpretation of resulting data.
5. Map genes relative to other genes by interrupted mating, natural gradient of transfer and variations of these techniques.

Conjugation
Problem 1

Various strains of bacteria were incubated on plates containing minimal media plus several amino acids. From the pattern of growth, answer the following questions regarding the genotype of each strain.

What are the genotypes of colonies 1-4 with respect to arg, met, asp and ile?

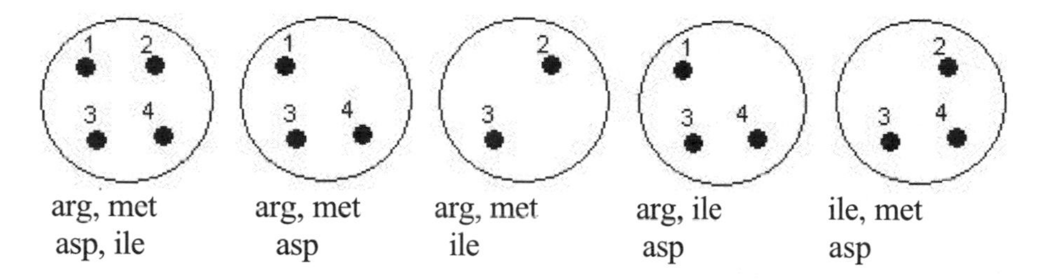

The following plates show bacterial strains that have been replica plated on minimal media plus the indicated mixture of amino acids and antibiotics.

Determine the genotypes of colonies 1-4 with respect to arg, met, pen and str.

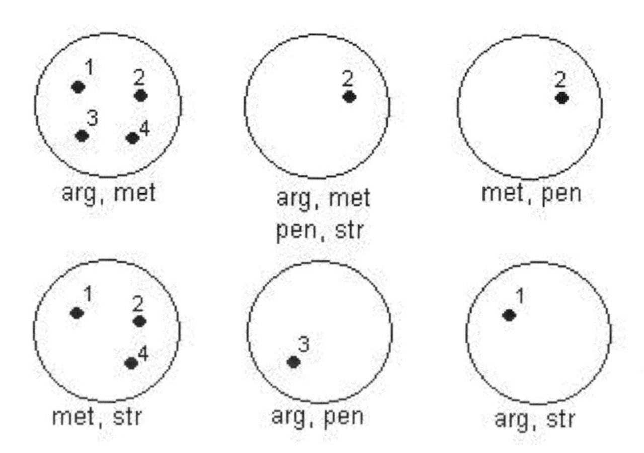

The plates shown below contain different sugars as carbon sources. Cells were first plated on minimal media with glucose as the carbon source (Masterplate) and then replica plated onto plates with lactose, mannose or arabinose (no glucose).

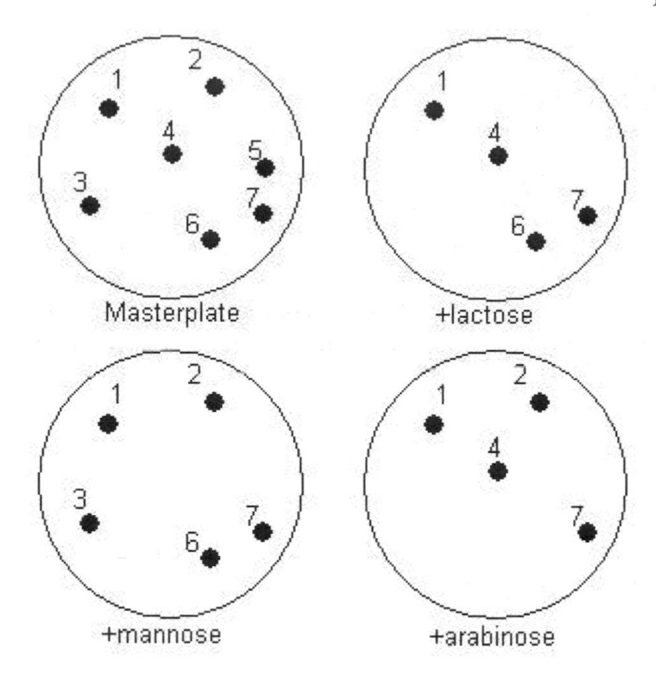

Which colony has the genotype *lac- man+ ara+*?

Which colony has the genotype *lac+ man- ara+*?

Which colony has the genotype *lac+ man+ ara-*?

Which colony has the genotype *lac- man+ ara-*?

Which colony has the genotype *lac- man- ara-*?

Problem 2

Lederberg and Tatum made crosses by mixing pairs of strains. They used a C strain which was *arg-met+* and an E strain which was *arg+met-*. However, they did not know whether each of these strains was F-, F+ or Hfr. An example of the type of crosses they performed is shown below.

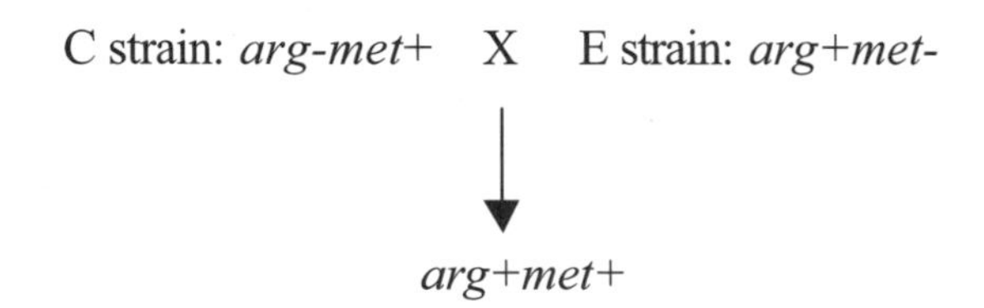

What type of cross would give you many exconjugants?

Which of the following crosses will give you only a few exconjugants?

What kind of crosses will give no *arg+ met+* exconjugants? (select from the choices below).

F+ x F+	**F- x Hfr**	**F+ x Hfr**
F- x F-	**F+ x F-**	**Hfr x Hfr**

The table shown here contains the results of all possible crosses (0=none; F=few; M=many). From the questions you just answered, you should now be able to identify which strains are F+, F-, and Hfr.

	E1	E2	E3	E4	E5
C1	F	0	M	F	0
C2	0	M	0	0	M
C3	0	F	0	0	F
C4	F	0	M	F	0
C5	0	F	0	0	F

Bonus Question

What we are looking for in our exconjugants are the recombinants of the E strains, *arg+met-* with the C strains, *arg-met+*. What type of media should be used to select for the prototrophic exconjugants?

Problem 3

From the time that Hfr and F- cells are combined, the number of markers transferred for each mating pair depends on how long the two cells stay conjoined. The mating can be interrupted at specified times after the start of mating by vigorous shaking, frequently accomplished by blending. Without such mixing the disruption of the mating pairs occurs naturally generating a gradient of transfer.

In the following experiment, a prototrophic Hfr strain (streptomycin sensitive) is mated to a streptomycin resistant F- strain auxotrophic for methionine, leucine, and cysteine. A pipette is used to distribute cells to each of the plates shown below, each containing minimal media with streptomycin, methionine, and cysteine added in order to select only for leucine prototrophs.

Aliquots of culture A (Hfr cells only), culture B (Hfr cells + F- cells), and culture C (F- cells only) are added to the three plates containing streptomycin, methionine, and cysteine. The plates are then incubated. The results are shown in the following illustration. Genotypes: (Hfr: *str-s, met+ leu+, cys+*) (F-: *str-r, met-, leu-, cys-*).

A: str, met, cys
No colonies

B: str, met cys
375 colonies

C: str, met, cys
No colonies

Why were no colonies observed after plating the Hfr strain on plate A above?

Why were no colonies observed after plating the F- strain on plate C above?

Why were cells able to grow on plate B?

The mating mixture produced 375 exconjugant colonies that replaced the *leu-* allele of the F- strain with the *leu+* allele of the Hfr strain. Additional markers may have also been transferred and could be checked by replica plating.

To measure the time of entry of each of the markers, matings between the Hfr and F- strains can be interrupted at various time points and plated on selective media. Below is a graph of colonies versus time.

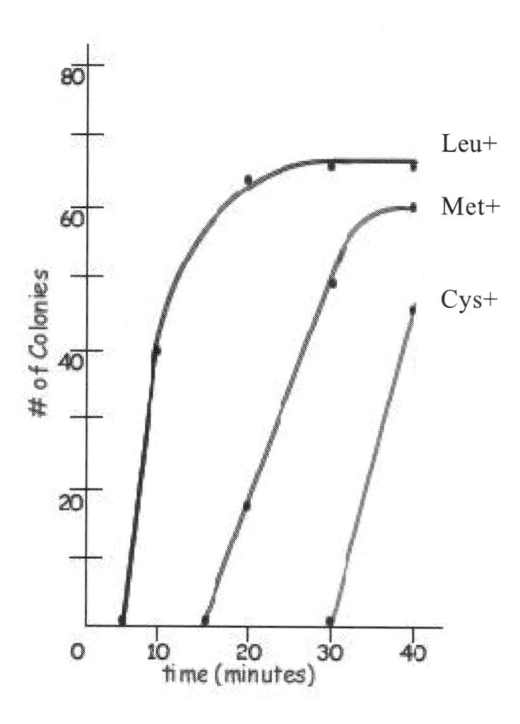

Draw a map below to indicate the order of the markers in the Hfr strain with respect to the origin.

Problem 4

An Hfr strain with genotype *met- leu+ his+ trp+* that transfers the met gene very late was mated with an F- *met+ leu- his- trp-* strain. After mating for 30 minutes, cells were plated on minimal media (MM) with the added nutrients listed below each plate. The number of colonies that grew on each plate are indicated.

Plate	**1**	**2**	**3**
Supplements	**His, Trp**	**His, Leu**	**Leu, Trp**
Colonies	**250**	**50**	**500**

What is the purpose of the methionine marker in this cross?

What markers are selected for on Plate 1?

What markers were selected on Plate 2?

What markers were selected on Plate 3?

Those markers closest to the origin are transferred first and yield the highest number of recombinant colonies. Based on the number of colonies on each plate above, determine the order of the markers in the Hfr strain with respect to the origin.

Problem 5

A small bacterial genome was mapped using 3 different Hfr strains and an F- *str^r^ ala- ade- bio- his- ile- val-*. Each of the Hfr strains was str^s and contained the wildtype alleles for all the markers. The matings were interrupted after 30 minutes and the exconjugants were selected on the following plates (the indicated nutrient is left out of the otherwise complete media + streptomycin).

Hfr: str^s *ala+ ade+ bio+ his+ ile+ val+* x F-: str^r *ala- ade- bio- his- ile- val-*

Mating	Missing Nutrient					
	Ala	Ade	Bio	His	Ile	Val
HfrA x F-	300	0	0	0	900	750
HfrB x F-	0	400	0	0	700	875
HfrC x F-	200	0	956	724	0	0

In the table above, some of the plates have no colonies. How can this be explained?

Consider the data from the Hfr A x F- cross. Which of the markers can be ordered using this cross?

What is the first marker to be transferred by Hfr A?

Order the three markers starting with ile.

What is the order of the markers indicated by the results of the Hfr B x F- cross?

What is the order of the markers indicated by the results of the third cross?

In every problem so far we have represented the bacterial chromosome as a circle. The original recognition of this fact comes from comparing the maps of different Hfr strains. As you can see from your results, the maps can only be reconciled as permutations from a common circular map, with the different Hfr strains having different origin points and directions of transfer. Use this information to construct a circular map.

Transduction
Problem 1

A generalized transducing phage is grown on a prototrophic strain and then used to transduce a recipient that is *arg-leu-gln-gua-thr-*. In this experiment *arg+* transductants will be selected by plating on media lacking arginine but containing all other supplements required by the recipient strain. This will be the master plate.

DONOR: *arg+ leu+ gln+ gua+ thr+*
RECIPIENT: *arg- leu- gln- gua- thr-*

MASTERPLATE: leu, gln, gua, thr (supplements)

59 colonies grew on this master plate. To test for co-transduction of the unselected markers, the colonies were replica plated to different media omitting one supplement at a time. The results are shown in the following table.

Supplements to Minimal Media					
Plate	leucine	guanine	glutamine	threonine	colonies
1	-	+	+	+	0
2	+	-	+	+	0
3	+	+	-	+	24
4	+	+	+	-	0

What does the absence of growth indicate on plate 1?

What does the presence of growth indicate on plate 3?

What is the co-transduction frequency (in percent) of *arg* and *gln*?

To develop a genetic map, let us now repeat the transduction experiment and make a new master by plating on media lacking leucine but containing all other supplements required by the recipient strain. This is our 2nd master plate. 73 colonies grew on this plate and were replica plated onto various plates containing the media indicated in the table below.

Supplements to Minimal Media					
Plate	arginine	guanine	glutamine	threonine	colonies
1	-	+	+	+	0
2	+	-	+	+	22
3	+	+	-	+	0
4	+	+	+	-	45

What is the co-transduction frequency (in percent) of *leu* and *gua*?

What is the co-transduction frequency (in percent) of *leu* and *gln*?

To finish our experiment, we will do one more transduction. In this 3rd master plate our media lacks guanine but contains all other supplements required by the recipient strain. 65

colonies grow on this plate which is replica plated onto various plates containing the media indicated in the table below.

Supplements to Minimal Media					
Plate	arginine	leucine	glutamine	threonine	colonies
1	-	+	+	+	0
2	+	-	+	+	20
3	+	+	-	+	13
4	+	+	+	-	0

What is the co-transduction frequency of *gua* and *gln*?

Using these co-transduction frequencies you have determined, order of the three markers: *arg*, *gua,* and *gln*.

Problem 2

In a transduction experiment, the donor strain is kan^r *lys+ arg+* and the recipient strain is kan^s *lys- arg-*. Transductants are plated on MM (minimal media) supplemented with kan (kanamycin), lys (lysine) and arg (arginine) and then replica plated on the plates shown below.

Supplements to Minimal Media				
Plate	**Kan**	**Lys**	**Arg**	**# of colonies**
Master	+	+	+	500
Replica 1	+	-	-	20
Replica 2	+	+	-	21
Replica 3	+	-	+	200

In the table below, fill in the number of colonies for each of the four genotypes.

Genotype	# of colonies
kanr arg+ lys+	
kanr arg+ lys-	
kanr arg- lys+	
kanr arg- lys-	

What is the co-transduction frequency of *kan* and *arg*?

What is the co-transduction frequency of *kan* and *lys*?

Problem 3

This problem is a simulation and can only be done on the *Interactive Genetics* CD-ROM.

Problem 4

Frequently, mutations are so close together that it's impossible to determine their order with respect to a nearby marker by simply using conjugation or transduction.

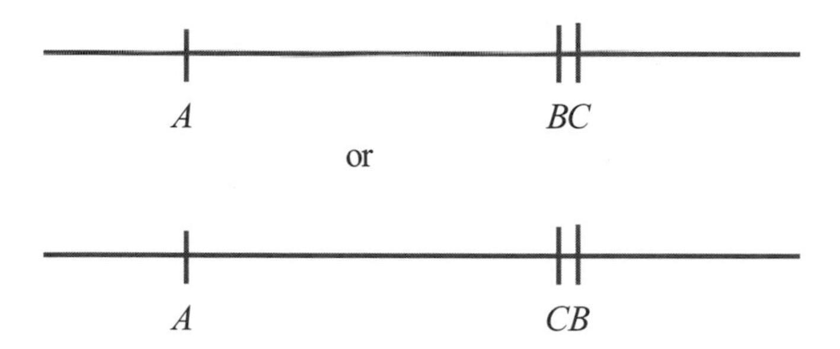

In the illustration above it is difficult to determine if *B* is closer to *A* or *C* is closer to *A*. The co-transduction frequency between *A* and *B* would be about the same as the co-transduction frequency between *A* and C. However, reciprocal three factor transductions can be used to determine the order of these markers.

Unlike in plants and animals, reciprocal transductions in bacteria do not refer to switching markers between sexes. Instead, in bacteria we refer to switching the markers between the donor and recipient. That is, in Transduction 1 the donor may be *B+C-* and the recipient *B-C+*, while in Transduction 2 (the reciprocal) the donor may be *B-C+* and the recipient *B+C-*. Having the markers in trans is essential for this experiment since it forces a crossover between the two tightly linked markers (*B* and *C*) to generate a prototroph. The outside marker will be *A+* in the donor and *A-* in the recipient in all transductions.

In the two reciprocal transductions shown below the order is assumed to be ABC. Draw an X in the appropriate places to generate prototrophic (*A+B+C+*) transductants for each experiment.

Transduction I: Donor: *A+B+C-* Recipient: *A-B-C+*

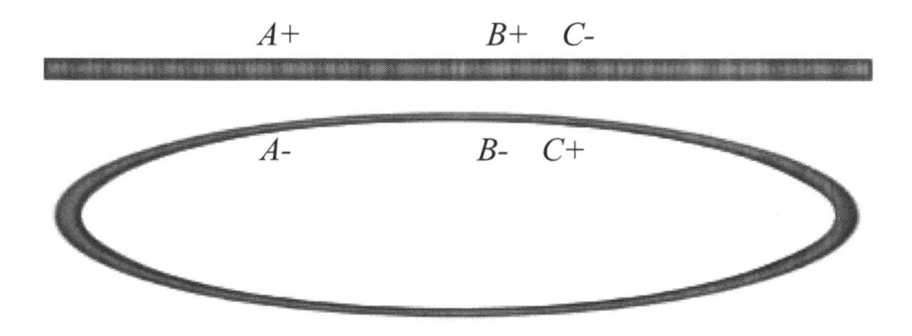

Transduction II: Donor: *A+B-C+* Recipient: *A-B+C-*

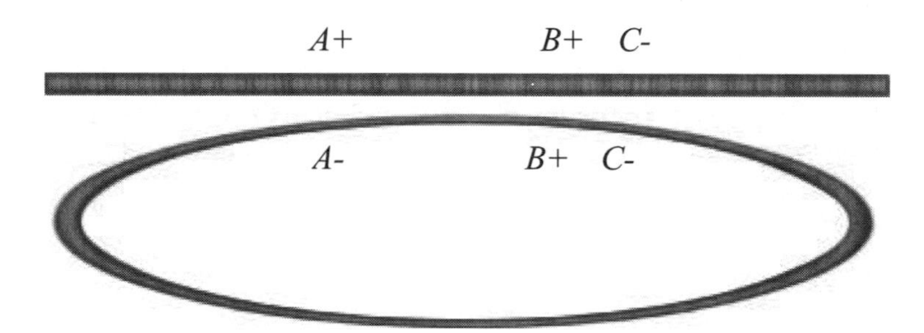

Notice that in Transduction I, prototrophs were generated with only two crossovers whereas in Transduction II, four crossovers were required to generate *A+B+C+*. This is true only when the order is ABC.

Now we will see what happens if the order is *ACB*. Again, draw X's in the appropriate places to generate prototrophic (*A+B+C+*) transductants.

Transduction I: Donor: *A+B+C-* Recipient: *A-B-C+*

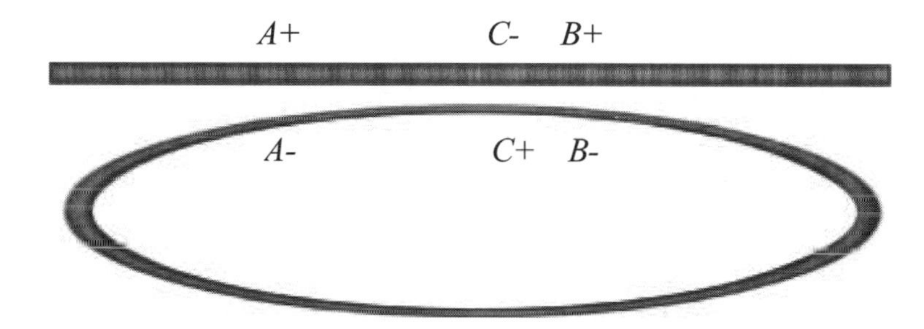

Transduction II: Donor: *A+B-C+* Recipient: *A-B+C-*

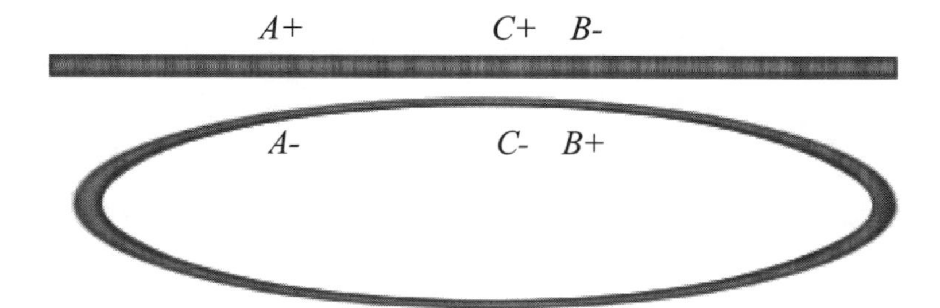

Notice that Transduction I prototrophs were generated with four crossovers whereas in Transduction II only two crossovers were required to generate *A+B+C+*.
A minimum of two crossovers is required to incorporate genes from the donor fragment into the circular recipient chromosome. This results in the frequencies of transduction we usually

observe. However, a situation that requires four crossovers will yield many fewer transductants or none at all.

You need to compare reciprocal transductions in order to determine which experiment gives you normal transduction frequencies and which gives you reduced frequencies. This example asks you to determine the frequencies using two different orders, although there is only one order.

Reciprocal transductions were used to order three mutations *(trp1, trp2,* and *trp3)* required for metabolism of tryptophan with respect to a nearby marker tyrosine *(tyr+)*. For each pair of mutants *(trp1 & trp2; trp2 & trp3; trp 1 & trp3)* a pair of reciprocal transductions will be made to order them with respect to *tyr*.

	Donor	Recipient
Transduction I.	*tyr+ trpx- trpy+*	*tyr- trpx+ trpy-*
Transduction II.	*tyr+ trpx+ trpy-*	*tyr- trpx- trpy+*

Experiment	x y	I	II
1	*trp1 trp2*	800	5
2	*trp2 trp3*	3	750
3	*trp1 trp3*	659	8

Which mutation, *trp1* or *trp2*, is closer to *tyr*?

Which mutation, *trp1* or *trp3*, is closer to *tyr*?

Which mutation, *trp2* or *trp3*, is closer to *tyr*?

Draw a map below to indicate the order of the three mutations with respect to *tyr*.

Biochemical Genetics

Goals for Biochemical Genetics:

1. Determine the number of genes coding for steps in a biosynthetic pathway. Use auxotrophic mutant strains to determine the number of complementation groups for a pathway.
2. Determine a biosynthetic pathway from nutritional studies that supplement with compounds that may be intermediates in the pathway.
3. Determine whether any of the genes are linked to each other.
4. Distinguish the metabolism of amino acids between anabolic (biosynthetic) and catabolic (degradative) reactions. Most human biochemical disorders show up from the loss of a catabolic enzyme. Auxotrophic mutant strains of microorganisms result from the loss of an anabolic enzyme.

Problem 1

Six Neurospora mutants were isolated that require vitamin B1 to grow. To determine whether the six mutants have mutations in different genes, complementation studies were performed. Heterokaryons were formed and tested for growth on minimal media.

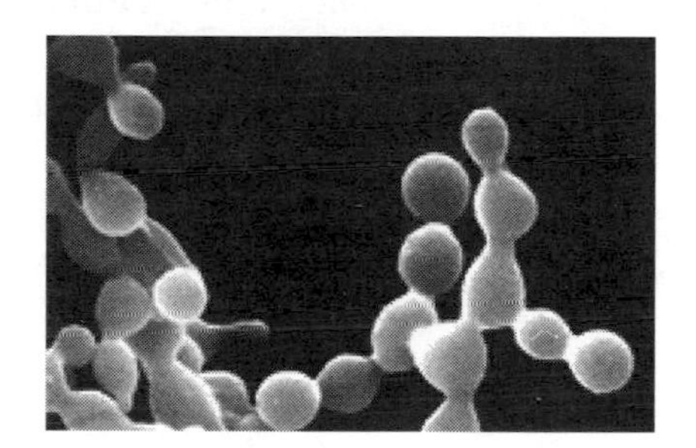

The following table shows the experimental results; + indicates heterokaryon growth and - indicates no heterokaryon growth in the absence of vitamin B1.

	A	B	C	D	E	F
A	-	+	+	-	+	+
B	+	-	+	+	-	-
C	+	+	-	+	+	+
D	-	+	+	-	+	+
E	+	-	+	+	-	-
F	+	-	+	+	-	-

Which mutants belong to the same complementation group as mutant A?

Which mutants belong to the same complementation group as mutant B?

Which mutants belong to the same complementation group as mutant C?

Which mutants belong to the same complementation group as mutant D?

How many complementation groups are there?

Would a heterokaryon formed from mutant A and the double mutant C,E grow on minimal media? The double mutant strain contains two gene mutations: the gene mutation in strain C and the gene mutation in strain E.

Would a heterokaryon formed from the double mutants A,B and C,F grow on minimal media?

Would a heterokaryon formed between the three double mutants A,E and B,C and C,D grow on minimal media?

Problem 2

You are a graduate student working in a Neurospora lab and have recently isolated five Neurospora methionine auxotrophs which each contain a single gene mutation. You set out to determine if any of the mutated genes in the Neurospora strains are linked. You decide to do this by crossing mutant strains and examining the phenotypes of the progeny.

You form a transient diploid by mating mutant strains (represented by the cross *ab*+ x *a*+*b*). The diploids then undergo meiosis immediately by sporulation. A diploid cell with a crossover in the interval between the linked *a* and *b* genes (in this example), will yield four genetically distinct spores. Three of them are still auxotrophs and only the *a*+*b*+ spore is phenotypically distinct as a prototroph. The frequency of prototrophs in a large collection of spores can be used to determine the map distance between two mutants.

The results of your crosses with the five Neurospora auxotrophic strains (A-E) in all combinations are shown below. For each cross, 1000 ascospores were plated on minimal media. The table shows the number of methionine prototrophs that you recovered from each cross.

	A	B	C	D	E
A	0	150	250	215	40
B		0	250	65	110
C			0	250	250
D				0	175
E					0

Since strains A-E are methionine auxotrophs, the prototrophic ascospores must have been produced from independent assortment or recombination between two mutated genes during meiosis. How many prototrophic ascospores would you expect from a cross if the recombinant progeny were produced by independent assortment?

For each of the linked genes in the table above, determine the map distance between them. Then, combine the information from each of the two factor crosses to assemble a map of the entire linkage group.

Problem 3

Wildtype Neurospora is orange when exposed to light during growth. You have isolated three albino mutants that are completely white even when grown in the presence of light. Using heterokaryon complementation studies, you find that these three strains have mutations in different genes, which you name *al-1*, *al-2*, and *al-3*.

You suspect that the albino mutants are white because they are unable to make the carotenoid pigment (known to cause the orange color). To test your idea, you seed the albino mutants on media supplemented with carotenoid pigment.

You are thrilled to find that supplementation with carotenoid pigment results in orange colored hyphae for all three albino mutants! Assuming carotenoid synthesis is affected in these mutant strains, you set out to determine which step in the biosynthetic pathway is blocked by each of the mutations.

Luckily, three precursors in the carotenoid pigment biosynthetic pathway had previously been discovered, although their order was unknown. To determine the order in which the precursors are converted into the carotenoid pigment, you grow the albino mutants on media supplemented with each of the three precursors.

You find that supplementing media with these different precursors restores wildtype color in some of the albino mutant. You compile your results into a simple table, where + indicates wildtype color and - indicates white color.

	Carotenoid pigment	**GGPP**	**Phytoene**	**PPP**
al-1	+	-	-	-
al-2	+	-	+	+
al-3	+	-	+	-

Use the data from your experiments to determine the order of the precursors as they appear in the biosynthetic pathway and which step in the biosynthetic pathway is blocked by each mutant.

Problem 4

Saccharomyces cerevisiae has played a fundamental role in human history and culture. For centuries, yeast has been used by humans for the rising of bread, and for the fermentation of wines and beers. Today yeast is used as a model organism for both genetic and cellular biology studies. Yeast are eukaryotes that grow simply as either single cells or colonies.

Saccharomyces cerevisiae can exist as either a haploid or a diploid. Both haploids and diploids are able to grow and divide by mitosis, through a process called budding. This differs from Neurospora where the diploid zygote is transient and quickly undergoes meiosis to form ascospores. In the haploid state there are 2 mating types, a and α. When an a cell and an α cell are brought together, they fuse to form a diploid cell. First the cellular membranes fuse, then the nuclei (yeast do not normally form stable heterokaryons). The diploid cell can grow and divide indefinitely. However, when nutrients are depleted or when environmental conditions become unfavorable, the diploid cells will undergo meiosis to form 4 haploid spores (a process called sporulation). The spores can be separated manually and tested directly for phenotype. Since they are haploid, their phenotype directly reflects their genotype.

Ten mutant yeast strains have been isolated that cannot grow on medium with galactose as the sole carbon source (galactose medium). The ten strains are named A-J. Each mutant was separately crossed to the others to form a set of diploid strains. The ability of the diploids to grow on galactose medium was used as a measure of complementation. The results of this experiment are given in the chart below.

Gal Mutants

	A	B	C	D	E	F	G	H	I	J
A	-	+	+	+	+	-	-	+	-	+
B		-	+	+	+	+	+	-	+	+
C			-	+	+	+	+	+	+	+
D				-	-	+	+	+	+	-
E					-	+	+	+	+	-
F						-	-	+	-	+
G							-	+	-	+
H								-	+	+
I									-	+
J										-

Are mutants A and B in the same complementation group?

Are mutants A and F in the same complementation group?

How many complementation groups are present?

To determine whether the four genes identified were linked to one another, each diploid strain was sporulated and 1000 random spores were analyzed for growth on galactose medium. The number of spores that were able to grow on galactose medium is indicated in the table below.

	A	B	C	D	E	F	G	H	I	J
A	0	250	0	0	0	0	0	250	0	0
B		0	250	250	250	250	250	0	250	250
C			0	0	0	0	0	250	0	0
D				0	0	0	0	250	0	0
E					0	0	0	250	0	0
F						0	0	250	0	0
G							0	250	0	0
H								0	250	250
I									0	0
J										0

Since we know certain strains contain mutations in the same gene, we can simplify the chart above to reflect the same data by grouping together mutants from the same complementation group. We will arbitrarily give each complementation group a gal gene designation as follows: Mutants A, F, G, I - gal 1; Mutants B, H - gal 4; Mutant C - gal 7; Mutants D, E, J - gal 10 (these designations are given based on actual gal genes in yeast).

	Gal1	Gal4	Gal7	Gal10
Gal1	0	250	0	0
Gal4		0	250	250
Gal7			0	0
Gal10				0

Is gal1 linked to gal4?

Gal 1 shows no wildtype recombinants with either gal7 or gal10. How can you explain this observation?

Analysis of 100,000 haploid spores produced from each of the crosses above were plated on galactose medium. Use this data to determine the map distance between gal1 and gal7, gal1 and gal10, and gal7 and gal10.

	Gal1	Gal4	Gal7	Gal10
Gal1	0	25000	35	16
Gal4		0	25000	25000
Gal7			0	18
Gal10				0

Problem 5:

This problem is a simulation and can only be done on the *Interactive Genetics* CD-ROM.

Population Genetics

Goals for Population Genetics:

1. Be able to relate allele frequencies at a gene to population homozygote and heterozygote frequencies.
2. Be able to use Chi-square test to determine if a population is in Hardy-Weinberg equilibrium.
3. Combine family studies with population frequencies to predict the chance a child will be homozygous for a disease allele.

Problem 1

Do you know your genotype with respect to your ABO or MN blood types? Will you consider these genotypes when you decide to marry? Most people are unaware of the alleles they carry for the majority of their genes. How do you study the genetics of animals in a natural environment, where family units are usually impossible to discern (e.g fish). Because of the lack of pedigree data, individuals are regarded only as samples from the larger population.

A population, consisting of interbreeding individuals in a prescribed geographical area, contains a reservoir of all the gene copies (alleles) that will give rise to the individuals in the next generation. In these and similar examples, the population's allele frequencies are used to predict the genotype frequencies of the individuals.

The reservoir of alleles for a single gene is referred to as the gene pool for that gene. The genotypes of individuals can be considered a random (unbiased) sampling from the gene pool, with a gamete representing a single sample from the gene pool. In the following sets of questions we are going to use a bowl of Ping Pong balls (whose different colors represent different alleles) to simulate random sampling.

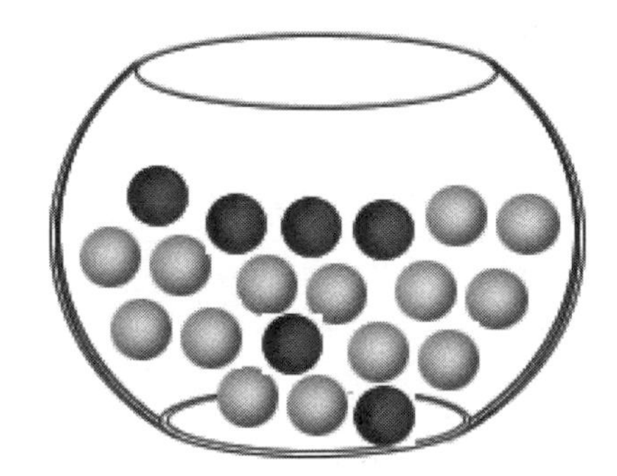

To represent diploid individuals subsequent questions will use pairs of samplings. What is the frequency of black ping-pong balls in the adjacent bowl?

Note that the probability of randomly obtaining a black ball, represented by p, is the frequency of black balls in the bowl.

What is the frequency of the white Ping-Pong balls in this bowl?

The frequency of white balls, represented by q, is the probability of randomly obtaining a white ball. Here black and white are the only colors of Ping-Pong balls in this bowl, and $p + q = 1$. To represent diploid individuals subsequent questions will use pairs of samplings.

What is the probability of picking two black balls (homozygous black)?

What is the probability of picking two white balls (homozygous)?

What is the probability of picking one white ball and one black ball (heterozygous) in either order?

As you have probably noticed, the sum of the probabilities found equals 1, that is $p^2 + 2pq + q^2 = 1$. This equation, which is derived from $(p + q)^2 = 1$ (when there are two alleles for a certain trait), describes the expected genotype frequencies of a population in Hardy Weinberg Equilibrium.

Problem 2

Consider this hypothetical population of 25 individuals of the FISH species. The sum total of all alleles present in the population is referred to as the population's gene pool. We will examine only one gene locus with two possible alleles: *F* for green color, and *f* for white color. In this population, the solid green fish are homozygous for *F*, the solid white fish are homozygous for *f*, and the spotted fish are heterozygous. Answer the following questions using the observed phenotypes.

Using the fish above, calculate p, the frequency of the green allele.

What is q, the frequency of the white allele? Recall, in the population above, 10 fish are *FF*, 5 fish are *ff*, and 10 fish are *Ff*.

To determine if this population is in equilibrium you need to determine the expected numbers using the Hardy Weinberg Equilibrium equation. To begin with, what is the expected frequency of *FF* individuals?

What is the expected <u>number</u> of FF individuals in this population?

What is the expected number of *ff* fish? What is the expected number of *Ff* individuals?

To find whether or not the population depicted above is in HWE (Hardy-Weinberg Equilibrium), we will perform a Chi Square (χ^2) test, using expected and observed values of each genotype. The χ^2 test is used to determine whether deviation from expected values are due to chance alone. If the deviations are too large we conclude that something besides chance is involved and the population is not in HWE. What is the value of χ^2 for this example? This χ^2 value can be converted into a probability value. To do this, we need the number of degrees of freedom (df) for the particular χ^2 test. The df equals the number of variables - 1. Although there are three genotypic classes their numbers are determined by only two variables (p and q). Therefore the degrees of freedom is 1. Using a χ^2 distribution chart, determine the probability (the p value) of obtaining these deviations due to chance alone. From your χ^2 test, is the population depicted above in Hardy Weinberg Equilibrium (HWE)?

Problem 3

Men are from Mars. Women are from Venus. When Mars and Venus collide, a new population arises. The allele frequencies on Mars and Venus differ. In the following problem, two alleles of a gene are represented by gray and blue ping-pong balls.

Mars Venus

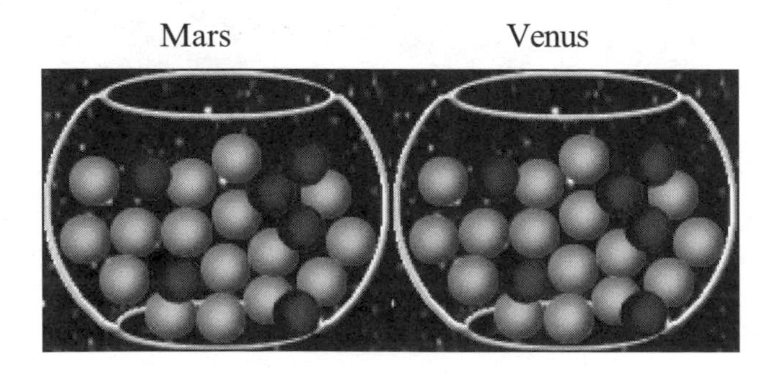

Predict the genotype frequency for homozygous gray in the new population.

What proportion of homozygous blue individuals do you expect in the new population?

What is the proportion of heterozygotes you expect the new population to have?

If the new population breeds only among themselves, will the next generation be in Hardy-Weinberg Equilibrium?

Problem 4

The ability to taste the chemical phenylthiocarbamide (PTC) is an autosomal dominant phenotype. Tasters can detect it as extremely bitter, while nontasters cannot detect it at all. The genotype frequency of the homozygous recessive individuals (nontasters) in the U.S population is 0.35 or 35%. Note that this population is in Hardy Weinberg Equilibrium (HWE) for this trait. What is the allele frequency for the nontaster allele?

q is commonly used to represent the allele frequency of the recessive (nontaster) allele. q^2, therefore, represents the genotype frequency of the homozygous recessive, nontaster individuals with a value of 0.35 . What is the allele frequency for the dominant taster allele?

p is commonly used to represent the allele frequency of the dominant (taster) allele. After finding allele frequencies, we will use these values to find genotype frequencies. Answer the following questions using p and q. What is the frequency of heterozygotes in the general population?

What is the frequency of heterozygotes among the PTC taster population only?

A PTC taster man whose mother is a taster while his father is not, marries a taster woman. Recall that PTC tasting is an autosomal dominant trait. What is the probability that their child will be a nontaster?

Problem 5

Red green colorblindness is a recessive sex-linked trait. In a given population that exists in HWE one in every eight males is colorblind. Using this information answer the following questions. What is the allele frequency for the red green colorblindness allele? (or, what is q?)

What proportion of all women are colorblind?

In what proportion of marriages will all the males be colorblind but none of the females?

In what proportion of the marriages will all the males be normal and the females be heterozygous?

Molecular Markers

Goals for Molecular Markers:

1. Recognize the kinds of variation in DNA sequences between homologous chromosomes that can be used as codominant alleles, including restriction fragment site polymorphisms and variations in the number of repeat sequences.
2. Understand the techniques (Southern Analysis and PCR) used to detect these variations within a defined chromosome region.
3. Understand how molecular markers are used for linkage studies to locate a disease gene and to start the positional cloning of the gene
4. Use molecular markers to determine the genotype of an individual for disease prediction, for relationship studies between individuals, and for forensic identification of unknown individuals.

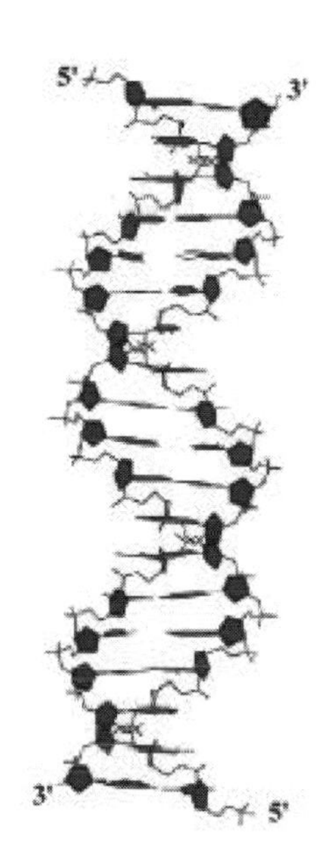

Problem 1

Restriction fragment length polymorphisms are identified by screening DNA isolated from members of families, using an array of different restriction enzymes. Random human genomic clones are then used as probes in a Southern blot. In the following problems you must identify the probe and restriction enzyme which gives rise to a polymorphism and then determine if the RFLP is linked to the inherited trait.

The DNA sample from each person is split into 6 tubes and digested with the following enzymes:

Apa I, Bam HI, Eco RI, Hind III, Sal I, Xma I

Gel electrophoresis separates the DNA fragments according to sizc. Denaturation of the DNA and transfer to nitrocellulose allows specific bands to be detected by hybridization with a radioactive probe (Southern blot). Choose the probe and restriction enzyme below that has an RFLP linked to the disease gene indicated by the pedigree.

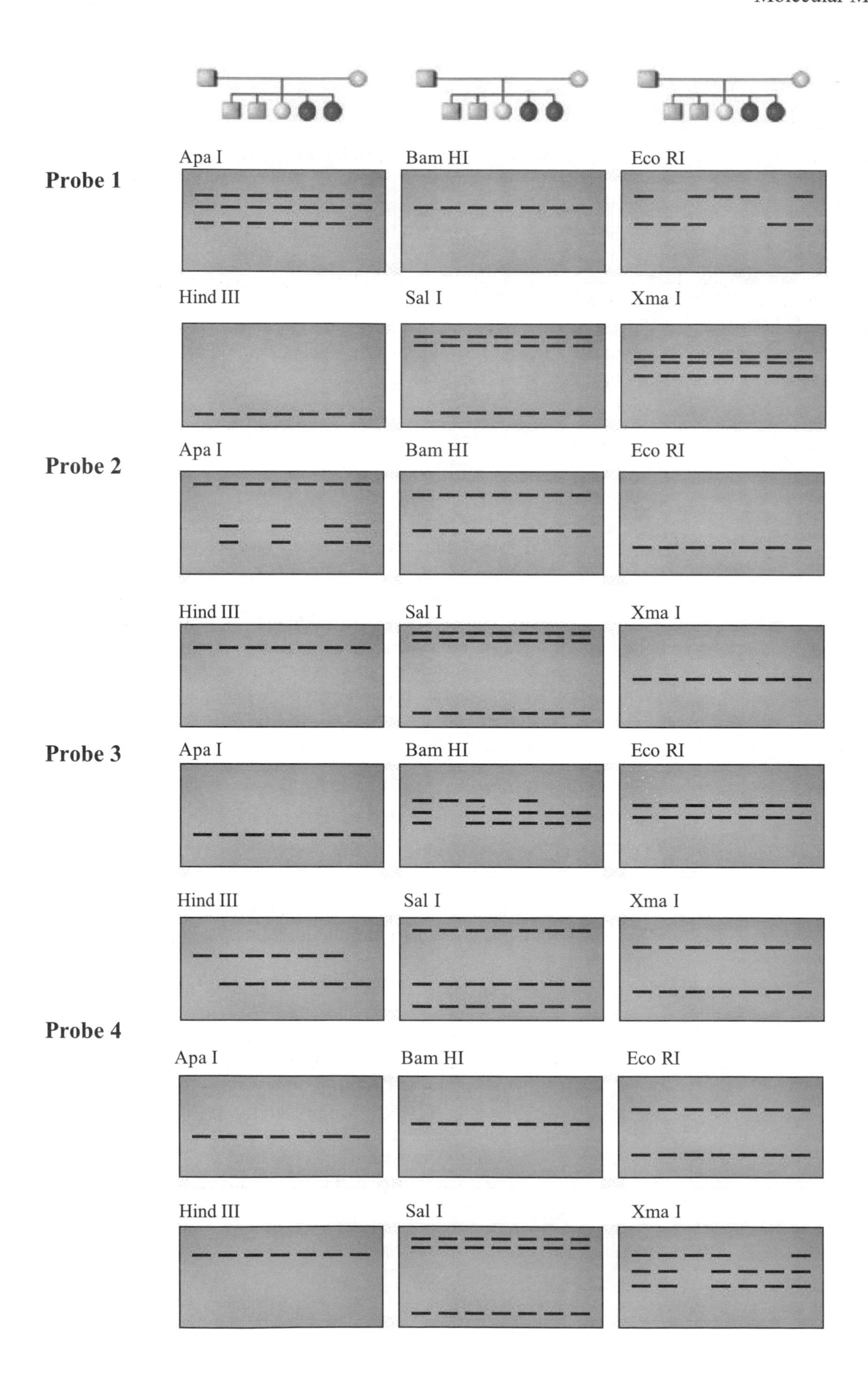
Probe 1
Apa I
Bam HI
Eco RI
Hind III
Sal I
Xma I
Probe 2
Apa I
Bam HI
Eco RI
Hind III
Sal I
Xma I
Probe 3
Apa I
Bam HI
Eco RI
Hind III
Sal I
Xma I
Probe 4
Apa I
Bam HI
Eco RI
Hind III
Sal I
Xma I

Problem 2

Part a

In the pedigree below, the presence of the rare recessive disease phenylketonuria (PKU) is indicated by filled symbols. Using the A/a above, assign genotypes based on the pedigree analysis.

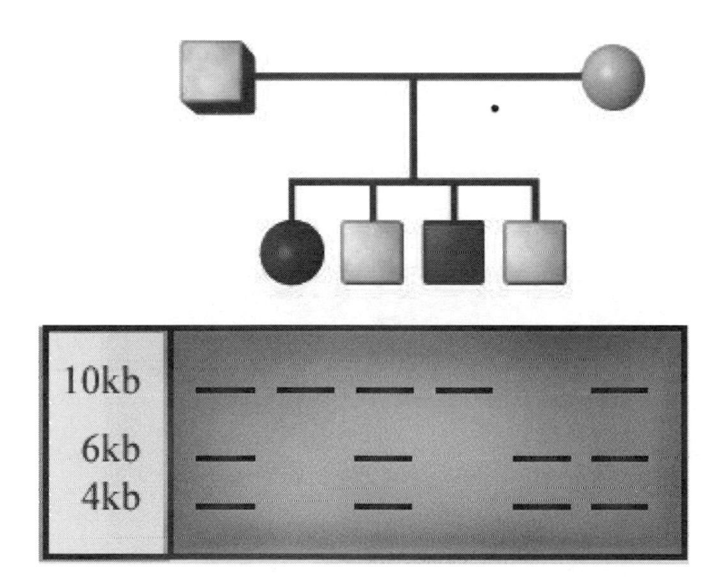

DNA was obtained from each of the individuals in the pedigree above, digested with a restriction enzyme and probed with a fragment known to hybridize to a linked RFLP. Analysis of the Southern blot above in conjunction with the pedigree allows determination of the linkage between the A/a gene and the RFLP shown. Focus first on the affected children. Use this information to determine the coupling (linkage) in each of the parents and then in the unaffected children. On the parental chromosomes shown below, fill in the galactosemia alleles (A/a) and the RFLPs (10 or 6-4) on the chromosomes to indicate linkage.

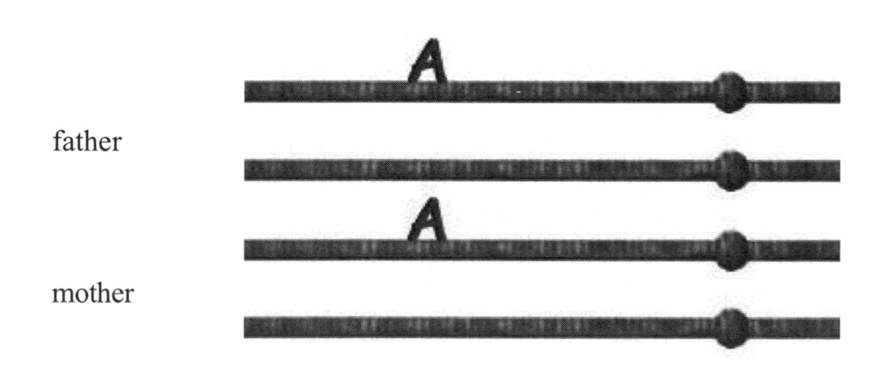

Part b

As a second example, let's look at linkage between the gene causing galactosemia and a nearby RFLP. In the pedigree above, the presence of the rare disease galactosemia is indicated by filled symbols. Using A and a, assign genotypes to each individual.

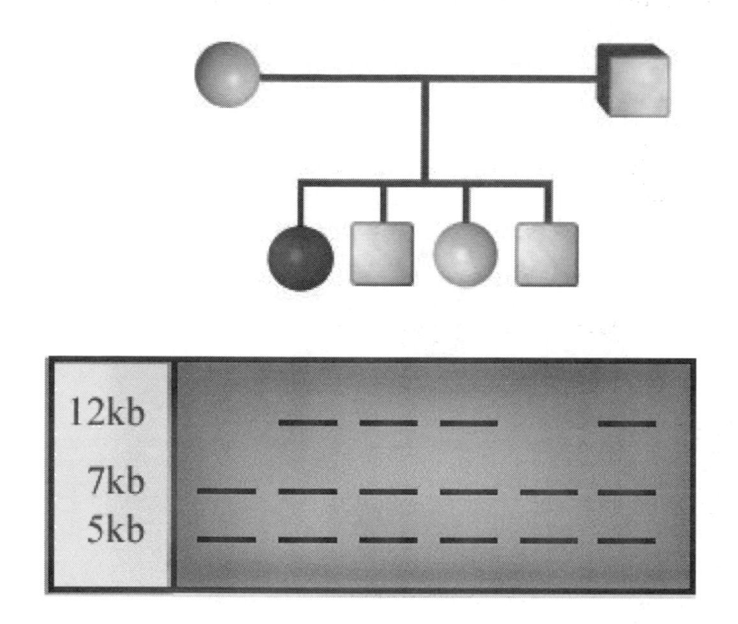

DNA was isolated from each of the individuals in the pedigree above and a probe from a linked RFLP was used in a Southern analysis to determine the genotype of each of the members of this family. On the parental chromosomes shown below indicate the linkage between the galactosemia alleles (A/a) and the RFLPs (12 or 7-5).

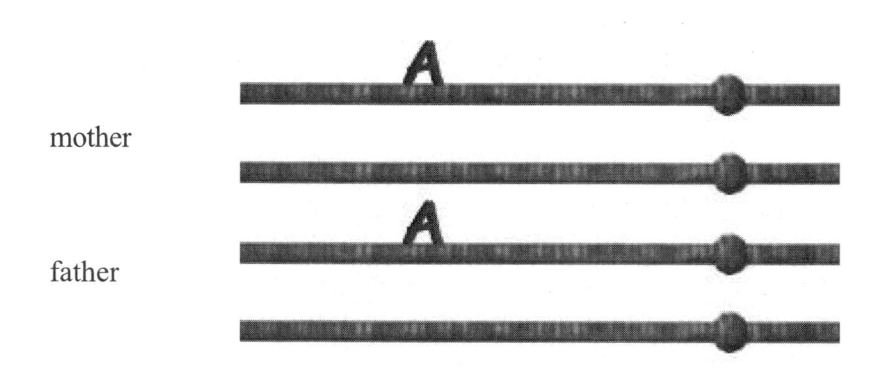

What is the probability that child 3 is a carrier of galactosemia? (Assume the RFLP is tightly linked to the galactosemia gene and no crossing over occurs between them).

What is the probability that child 4 is a carrier of galactosemia? (Again assume tight linkage and no crossing over.)

Problem 3

Part a

The pedigree shown below traces the inheritance of polydactyly, associated with a dominant, autosomal allele (D). Southern analysis reveals a closely linked RFLP. On the chromosomes shown below, indicate this linkage by typing in the appropriate D or d alleles and the linked 8 kb (8) or 6-2 kb (6-2) alleles.

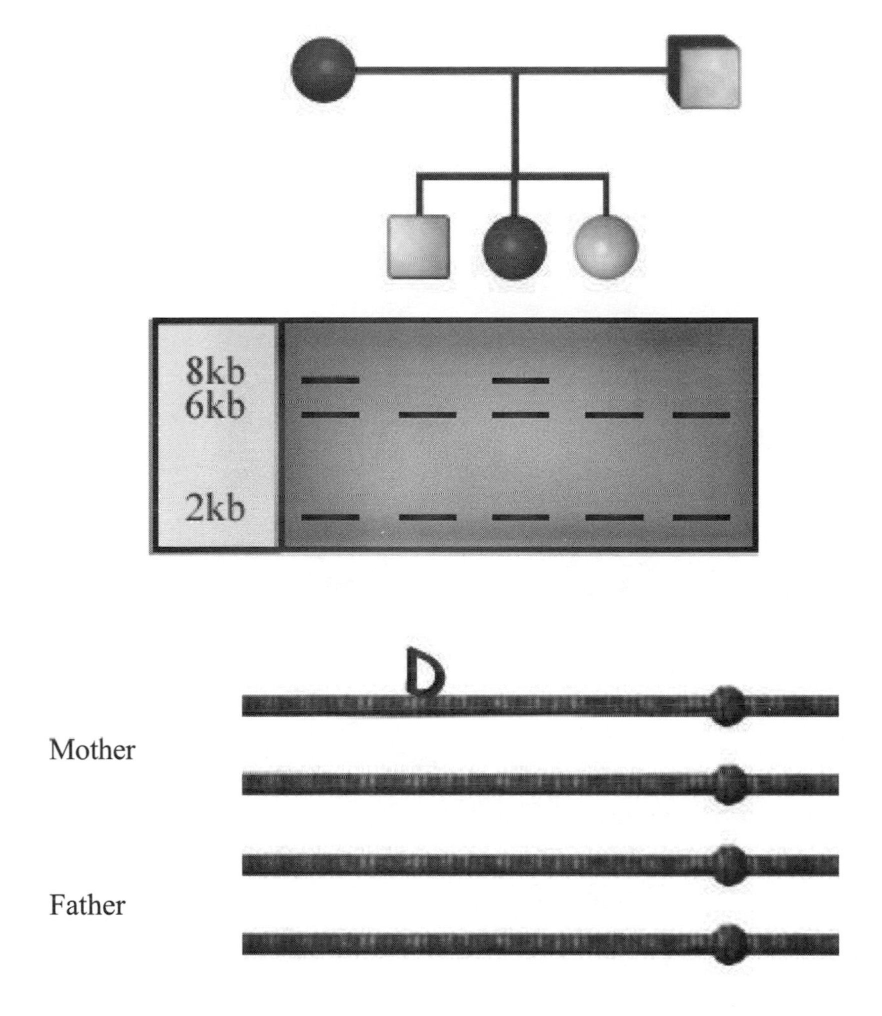

Use the Southern blot above to determine which children are heterozygous for polydactyly.

Child 1 marries a normal female and they are expecting a child, what is the probability the child will be affected?

Child 2 marries a normal male and they are expecting a child, what is the probability the child will be affected?

Would analysis of this RFLP in the fetus help them determine whether their child will have polydactyly?

Part b

Red-green colorblindness in humans is caused by an X-linked recessive allele (c). An STRP (small tandem repeat polymorphism) was found that is closely linked to the colorblindness gene. Assume no recombination in this problem. PCR was used to amplify this region of the genome for the individuals in the pedigree. Assign the appropriate alleles (C, c or Y) and linked STRPs (6 or 7) on the parental chromosomes below.

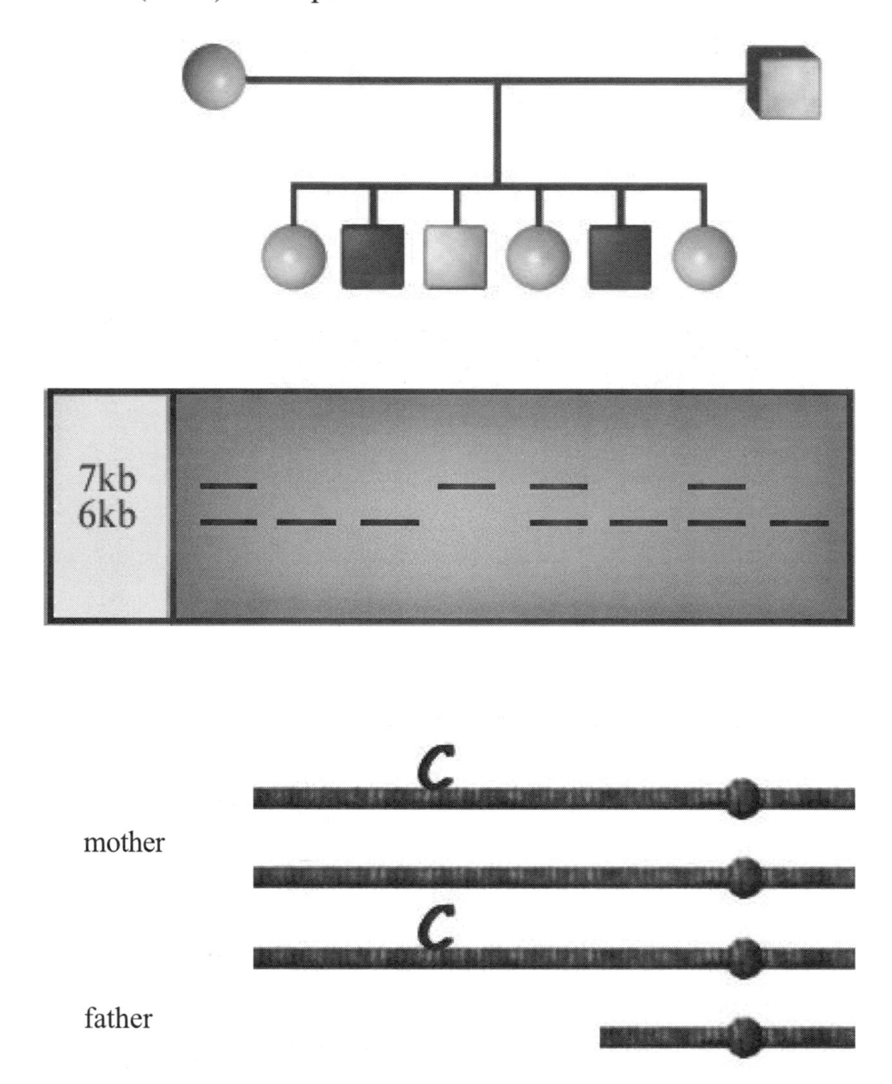

Use the gel above to determine which children are heterozygous.

Child 1 marries a normal male and they are expecting a child. What is the probability their child will be colorblind?

They find out that their baby will be a boy. Would analysis of this STRP in the baby help them determine whether their child will be colorblind?

Problem 4

You have recently identified two molecular probes (A and B) that hybridize to chromosome 12 in yeast. Although the loci are linked, you suspect they may be far enough apart to measure recombination. To test this, you mate two haploid strains to produce a diploid, which is then induced to undergo meiosis. You examine 100 meiotic haploid spores by Southern blotting and find the results shown on the next page.

Pattern	# spores	Probe A	Probe B
1	44	8 kb, 1kb	4 kb
2	7	9 kb	4 kb
3	42	9 kb	4.4 kb
4	7	8.1 kb	4.4 kb

You notice immediately that four patterns are discernable and that these are found at different frequencies. Using the information in the table, determine the genotype of the diploid cell formed from the two haploid parents. Write the linked alleles on the chromosomes below.

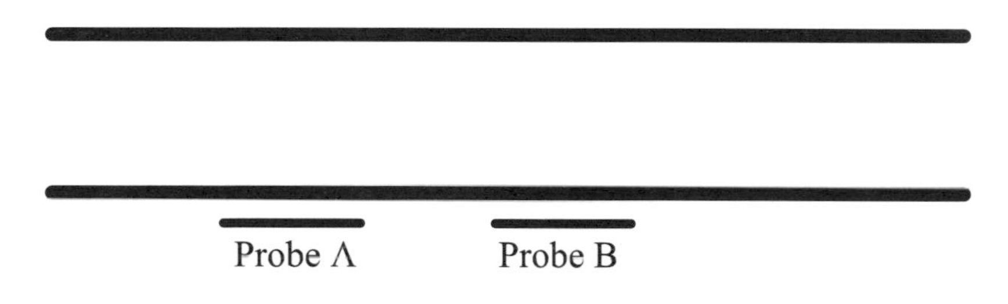

Using the data in the table, determine the distance between locus A and locus B.

Problem 5

Individuals with Duchenne's muscular dystrophy (DMD) are missing an important structural 'glue' of skeletal muscle. This makes them susceptible to muscle tears, and leads to the progressive death of muscle tissue. Many patients show pseudo hypertrophy (false muscle enlargement), especially in the calves, as muscles die and are replaced by fat and connective tissue. Almost all are confined to a wheelchair by the age of 10, and most die in their twenties, as their respiratory muscles fail.

Although the gene leading to DMD has been cloned and sequenced (dystrophin located on the X chromosome) and many mutations can be detected directly, not all alleles have been identified. In these cases, a linked polymorphism can be used to determine probabilities. Suppose in the following family an STRP located 6 map units away has been identified.

Answer the following questions taking into account any recombination that may occur. Note that all known disease alleles are recessive, appearing primarily in males.

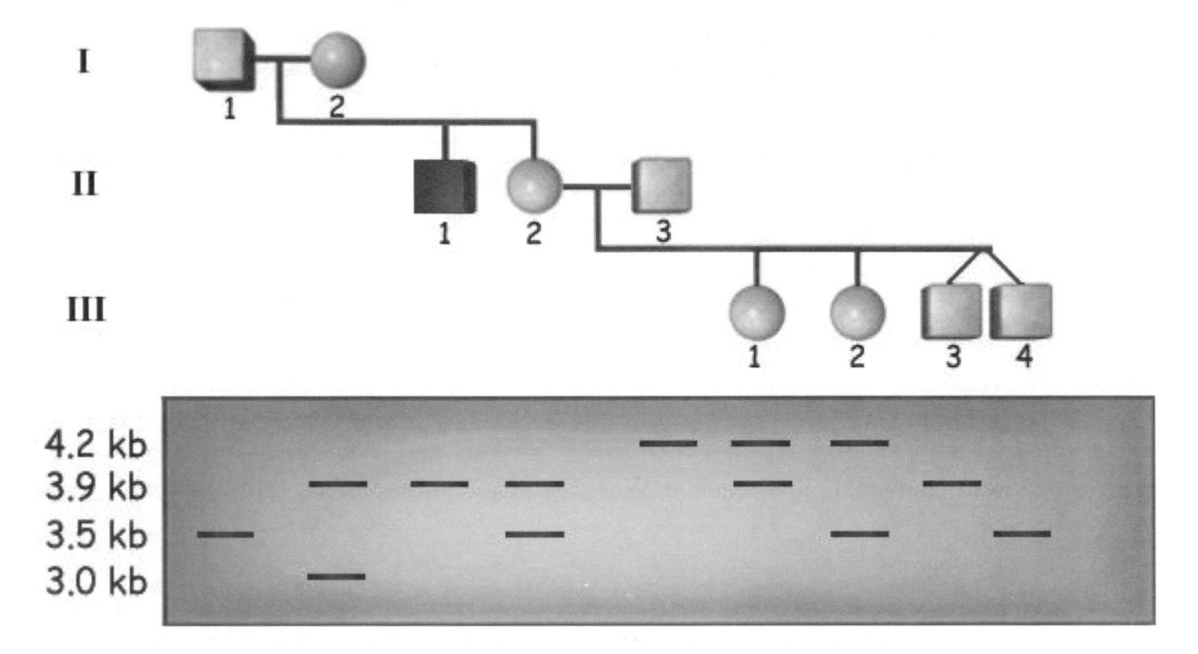

Roya (II-2) and Fardad (II-3) are in genetic counseling, after finding out she is pregnant with twin boys. Roya's brother has DMD and it is believed to be inherited from their mother. What is the probability that Roya is a carrier? Remember, the polymorphism shown is known to be 6 map units from the DMD gene. Assume there is no crossing over in the mother I-2 leading to the child II-1.

Roya has two unaffected girls. What is the probability that her daughter Sonya (III-1) is a carrier for DMD?

What is the probability that her second daughter Kate (III-2) is a carrier for DMD?

Roya is concerned about her twin boys. The first question she asked the genetic counselor was if the twins were identical or fraternal. Based on the gel above, how would you answer this question?

What is the chance the first twin (III-3) has DMD?

What is the chance the second twin (III-4) has DMD?

Problem 6

Megan, a nineteen year old, was found severely beaten off the side of a small rural road by a patrol officer. She was taken immediately to the nearest hospital, where she was treated for her injuries and it was discovered that she had also been raped. A semen sample was recovered and stored for DNA analysis.

Two men seen in the area at the time of the crime were brought in for questioning. They claimed to have been together all through the night and knew nothing about the young woman. Blood samples were taken from both men and 4 STRPs were examined and compared with the semen sample.

Southern analysis of both the suspects blood samples (1 and 2) and the semen sample (S) was performed using well characterized STRPs. Allele frequencies determined using the FBI databases for the US population were then used for probability determinations (only alleles A, B and C shown). It is assumed these alleles are present in Hardy Weinberg Equilibrium. From the data below, can either suspect be excluded?

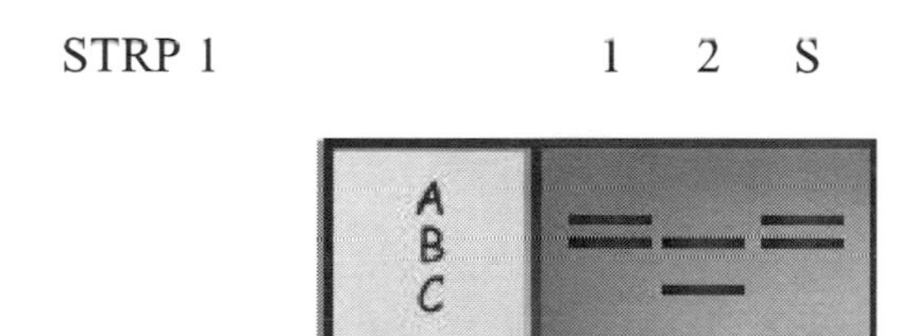

Frequency in US Population

Allele	Frequency
A	1/3
B	1/9
C	1/15

What is the probability that an individual would have the genotype consisting of STRP alleles A and B? Does this prove that Suspect 1 committed the rape?

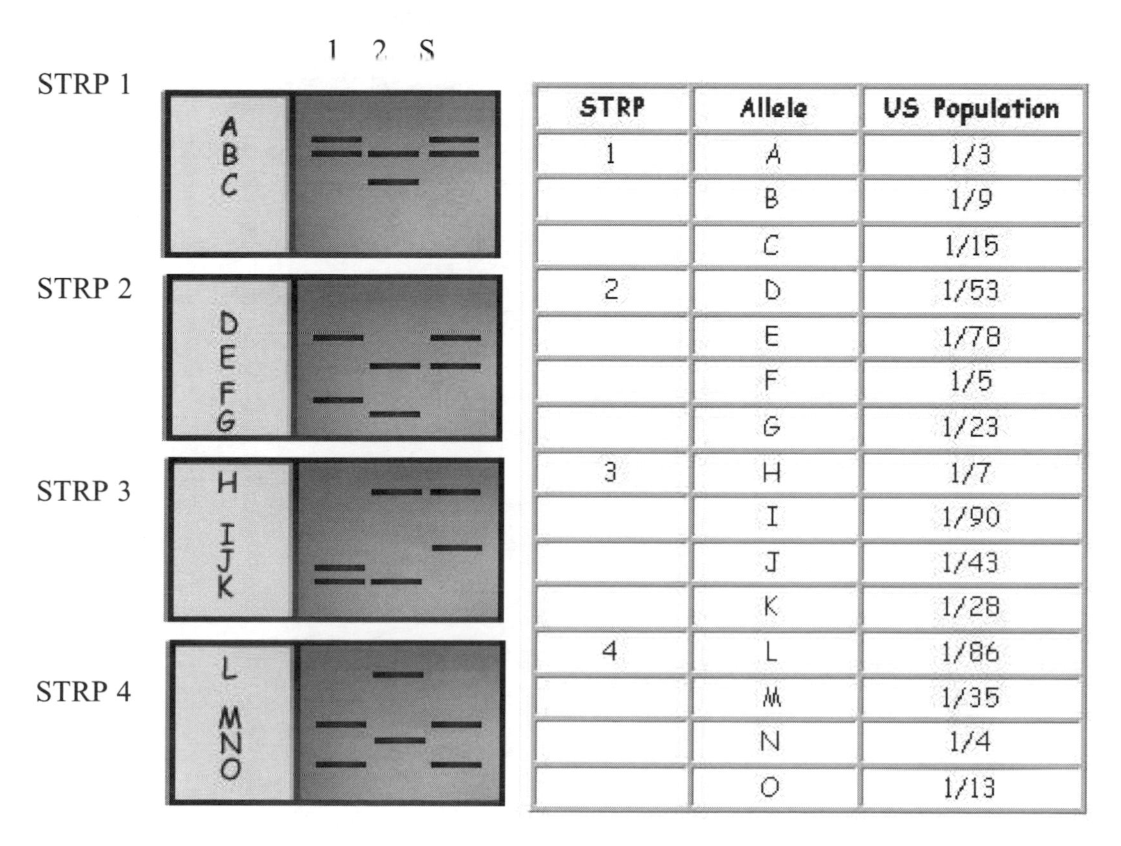

STRP	Allele	US Population
1	A	1/3
	B	1/9
	C	1/15
2	D	1/53
	E	1/78
	F	1/5
	G	1/23
3	H	1/7
	I	1/90
	J	1/43
	K	1/28
4	L	1/86
	M	1/35
	N	1/4
	O	1/13

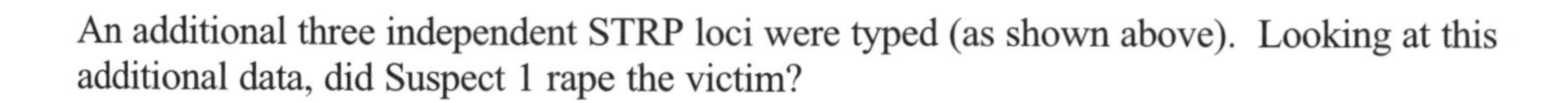

An additional three independent STRP loci were typed (as shown above). Looking at this additional data, did Suspect 1 rape the victim?

What is the probability of an individual in the US having the set of alleles found in the semen sample for all four STRPs?

In a population of 6 billion (the current population of the earth), how many individuals will have this pattern?

Medical Genetics

Goals for Medical Genetics:

1. Understand differences in classification of genetic diseases as chromosomal, single gene, or multifactorial in origin.
2. Understand how to use pedigree information to determine the mode of inheritance.
3. Interpret karyotypes to identify genetic diseases associated with chromosomal disorders.
4. Be able to understand and use in diagnosis molecular genetic techniques (ASO, FISH and PCR) that recognize mutant DNA causing genetic diseases.

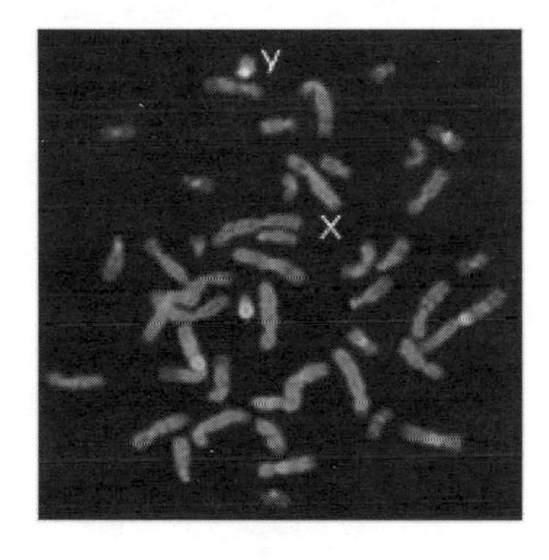

In this section, you will use case studies to see how the genetic techniques you have studied are used in medicine to help doctors form a diagnosis. To aid you in your diagnosis, the patient's clinical description and family history will be available to you. You will be able to perform various chromosomal and molecular genetic tests. At any point in your investigation, you can use the genetic reference database, and whenever you are ready, you may submit a diagnosis. You may want to take notes along the way to keep track of the information you have gathered.

Case I.

Frank and Mary Smith asked that their six-year old son George be seen by a pediatrician. His parents report that that he was slower than their other children to make his developmental milestones They had attributed his delays to a heart defect that he had when he was born that had required surgery in infancy. He has now started school and is having trouble because he is acting out and having some behavioral problems. They are concerned that he is not ready for school.

The pediatrician is concerned about the developmental delays but notes that George's language skills appear normal or even advanced for a six year old. He notes facial dysmorphisms (unusual facial features) that seem different from his family, including full lips, and puffy eyes. The pediatrician suggests that genetic tests be performed to rule out the following conditions for which further information is given:

Angelman syndrome
Di George syndrome
Down syndrome
Fragile X
PKU
Prader-Willi syndrome
William syndrome

Case II.

Han Chen and Yuh Nung Lee are referred to the Westside Fertility Clinic after a series of miscarriages. Han Chen is 43 and her husband is 38. Neither report any major health problems. Han Chen was born in Taiwan. Four brothers and sisters survive in her immediate family. Two siblings died shortly after birth and one was stillborn. Yuh Nung is an only child with no family history of infant mortality.

The clinic first evaluates Yuh Nung's sperm count and finds it is normal. During this evaluation Han Chen became pregnant, but loses the fetus after 3 months. Fetal tissue was obtained and examined for chromosomal abnormalities in the cytogenetics laboratory. Refer to the chromosomal section under disease reference for the list of chromosomal disorders that are considered.

Case III.

Sara and David Goldenstein have brought their daughter Rebecca in for her 6 month checkup. They are concerned as she has stopped gaining weight although she seems to have a healthy appetite. She has had frequent numerous colds and suffers from diarrhea. Sara and David are first cousins, but there is no other family data that is useful.

The physician finds no evidence of mental retardation. Based on the relatedness of the parents a recessive single Mendelian gene is suspected of causing the symptoms. Refer to the single gene section under disease reference for the list of disorders that may be considered in this case.

Case IV.

Jan de Broek (age 60) was referred for medical examination by social services after his arrest for vagrancy and disorderly behavior. Social services reports that he has lost his job, apartment and is currently homeless. Jan's family was contacted and states that his behavior seems similar to both his father and uncle at this age (they are both deceased).

The physician records several of the symptoms associated with senile dementia. These include episodes of severe irritability, forgetfulness, anxieties, ataxia and alcohol abuse.

Behavioral changes are among the hardest to diagnose; age related causes may include alcoholism, Alzheimer Disease and Huntington Disease. Schizophrenia is usually an early onset disorder, but should be considered if the patient history is uncertain. Further information is given in the disease reference list.

Molecular Biology

Gene Expression

Goals for Gene Expression:
1. Understand the molecular mechanisms by which the genetic information in a DNA sequence is converted to an amino acid sequence, or protein.
2. Be able to compare the similarities and differences between prokaryotic and eukaryotic transcription, and the proteins involved in this process.
3. Understand the mechanism of splicing, and how introns and exons are mapped in eukaryotic genes.
4. Understand how RNA is translated into a protein, and how changes in a gene's sequence can give rise to defective proteins.

Problem 1

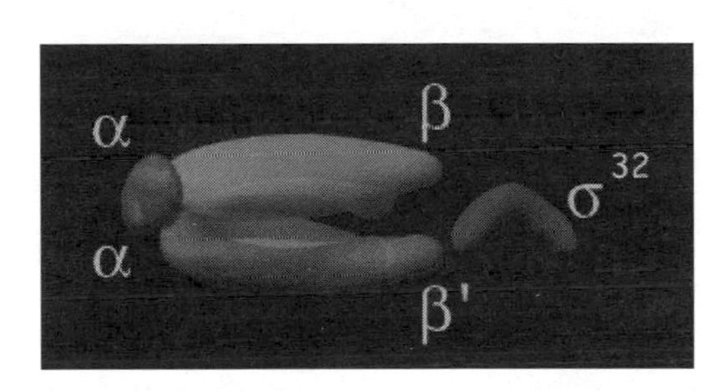

RNA Polymerase holoenzyme in the cell contains a sigma factor that is 70 kD (σ^{70}). However, there are several other sigma factors that recognize different promoter sequences and respond to specific cellular signals. One such sigma factor (σ^{32}) is activated in response to heat shock and recognizes promoters encoding chaperone proteins and proteases. Expression of these genes helps the cell deal with the heat denatured proteins to prevent further damage.

Comparison of promoter sequences found near genes that are transcribed under heat shock conditions revealed the recognition sequence of sigma-32. Shown below are 10 such promoter sequences. Determine the best consensus sequence for this promoter.

GCCTATATA
GCCCAACTT
CCCCATGTA
CCGCATTGA
CGCCACGTA
CCCGCTATT
CGCCATCTA
ACTCTTTTT
CCCTAGATA
CGCCATGTA

Promoters which have sequences that are a good match with the consensus bind RNA polymerase more often and lead to an increased amount of transcription. These are considered strong promoters. Which promoter sequence above has the best match to the consensus sequence? Which promoter would be considered the weakest promoter?

5' AGCCTAGCTCCATATAGAACGATCATCTAAG 3'
3' TCGGATCGAGGTATATCTTGCTAGTAGATTC 5'

You have recently found a new heat shock gene above and decide to use the consensus sequence to give a first approximation of the transcription start site (+1). Which nucleotide in the sequence above represents +1.

Write the appropriate substrates in a chemical equation below to describe formation of the first phosphodiester bond from this promoter.

Which end of the mRNA has the triphosphate group?

Only one of the two DNA strands is used as a template for RNA synthesis. Which strand is used in this example?

Problem 2

Exon-intron structure of genes can be determined in a number of ways. One method involves the comparison of <u>cDNA</u> with genomic DNA. This can be done either by DNA sequencing or Southern analysis. In this problem, the gene structure of calcitonin will be examined by Southern analysis.

Calcitonin is a peptide hormone synthesized by the thyroid gland and serves to decrease circulating levels of calcium and phosphate. This is achieved primarily by inhibiting bone decalcification (or resorption).

mRNA was isolated from human thyroid cells and converted to cDNA using reverse transcriptase. Isolation of the calcitonin cDNA was done by hybridization with the calcitonin genomic DNA (previously cloned). 10 subclones from the regions of the genomic DNA shown below were isolated and labeled for use as probes (1-10).

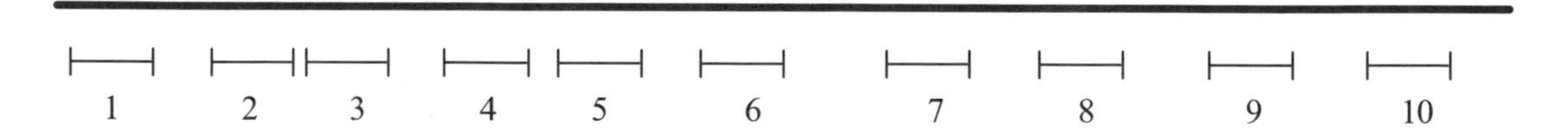

In order to determine where the calcitonin gene is located in the original genomic clone, Southern blots of the thyroid cDNA clone were hybridized with each of the ten probes (lane t, vector plus cDNA insert). A control of total genomic DNA digested with Not1 is included in lane g. See CD-ROM for the hybridization results.

The Poly-A site was found to be on the right side of the genomic DNA above, orienting the gene in a left to right direction. Use this information and the results from the Southern analysis to create an exon-intron map for the calcitonin gene.

Surprising results were observed when the same probes were used in conjunction with a cDNA clone isolated from neurons. Go to the CD-ROM to observe the results of Southern analysis on the neuronal cDNA clone (n) versus genomic DNA (g). Additional questions are available on the CD-ROM.

Problem 3

Hemoglobin is a tetrameric protein ($\alpha_2\beta_2$) which functions to carry oxygen in all vertebrates and some invertebrates. Each subunit of hemoglobin is associated with a prosthetic group, iron containing heme (in white above), which provides the ability to bind oxygen. Disorders associated with alterations to, or the disrupted synthesis of, hemoglobin are the most common genetic diseases in the world.

The β-globin gene is a relatively small gene, composed of three exons and two introns. One major class of hereditary disorders associated with hemoglobin is characterized by alterations in the amino acid sequence of β-globin but not the amount (structural variants). A second major class is characterized by a reduced level of hemoglobin (thalassemias), due to either mutations affecting transcription or splicing. In the following problem, β-globins were obtained from mutant hemoglobins. Use your knowledge of gene expression to help determine the cause of each of the mutations described.

Blood samples were collected from individuals homozygous for several distinct hemoglobin disorders. Protein from each sample was electrophoresed through either a native polyacrylamide gel or an SDS gel (shown below) and the separated proteins transferred to nitrocellulose. β-hemoglobin was then detected using antibodies (western analysis).

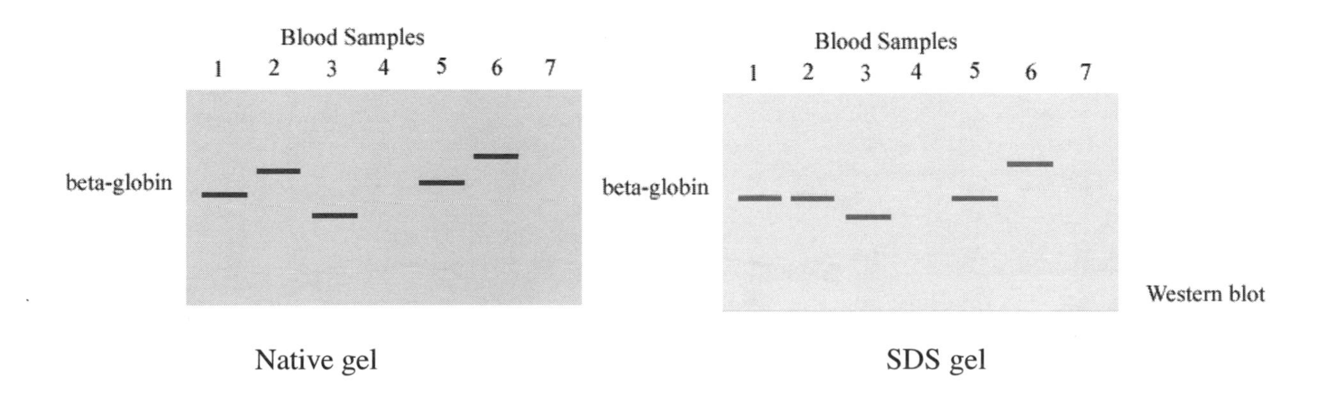

The first lane (blood sample 1) contains wildtype β-globin. Which lanes from 2-7 above represent structural changes in β-globin?

Compare the sample in lane 2 on a native versus SDS gel. Do these results suggest a change in the length of the polypeptide or the charge of the polypeptide?

Compare the sample in lane 3 on a native versus SDS gel. Do these results suggest a change in the length of the polypeptide or the charge of the polypeptide?

DNA and RNA samples were then examined by Southern and Northern blotting to detect changes in the DNA or RNA.

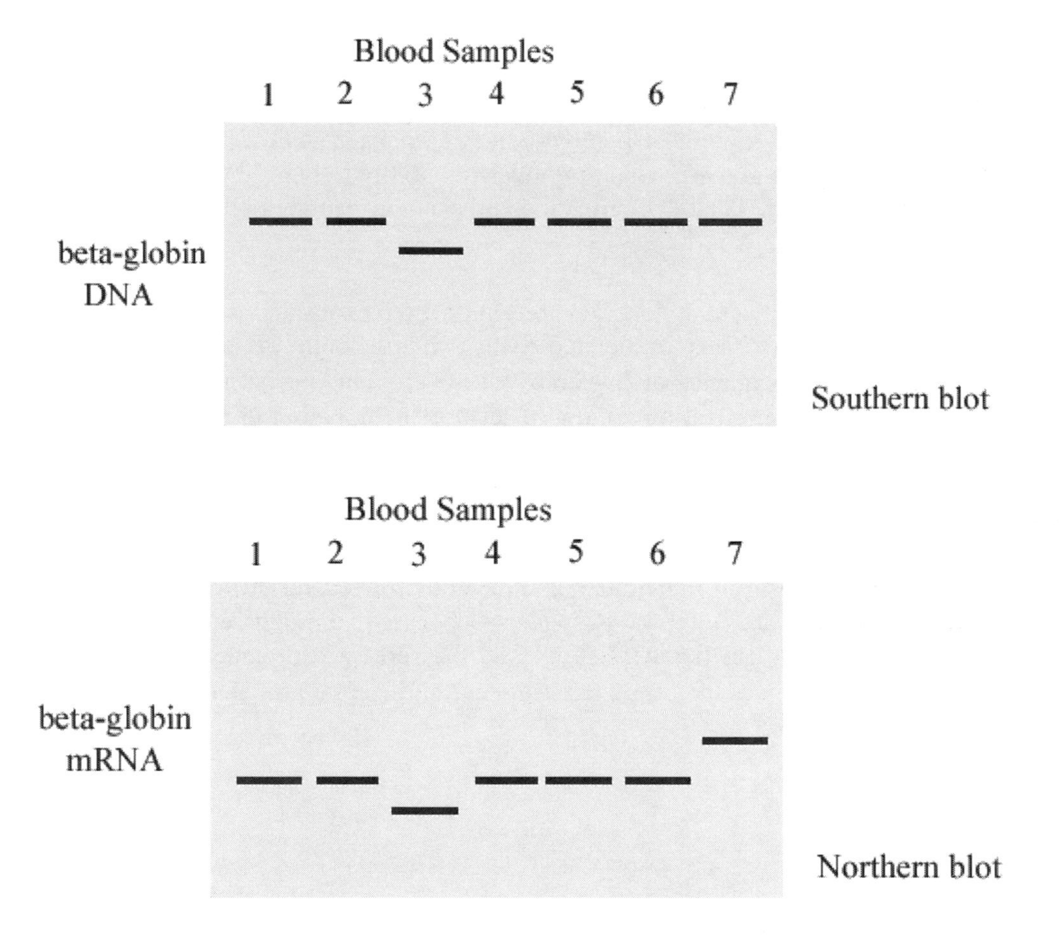

Again, the first lane contains a wildtype sample. To begin, let us examine sample 2 in detail. You have already determined the β-globin polypeptide differs from the wildtype by a charge change. Does the Southern blot detect any difference in sample 2 from wildtype?

Does the northern blot detect any changes in mRNA length in sample 2?

DNA from sample 2 was analyzed by dideoxy sequencing and compared to the wildtype gene. A single mutation was found in exon 1, as shown below (only the nontemplate strand is shown). Use the genetic code to determine whether this mutation represents a nonsense mutation (stop codon), missense mutation (amino acid substitution) or a frameshift mutation (insertion or deletion).

wildtype ATG GTG CAC CTG ACT CCT GAG GAG AAG TCT GCC

Sample 2 ATG GTG CAC CTG ACT CCT AAG GAG AAG TCT GCC

Now look at samples 3-7 and determine which fit the following descriptions. Which of the samples above could be explained by a nonsense mutation?

Which of the samples can be explained by a deletion of more than a few nucleotides?

Sickle cell anemia is known to be caused by a mutation which changes a glutamate codon at amino acid 6 to a valine. Which sample above is consistent with the sickle cell allele (HbS)?

Many thalassemias are caused by mutations that effect splice sites. Which sample above would be consistent with a splicing mutation?

The only sample that has not yet been identified is sample 6. What explanation is consistent with the results obtained for sample 6 above?

Molecular Biology

Gene Cloning

Goals for Gene Cloning:

1. Review the use of restriction enzymes and be able to use restriction enzymes to make a physical map of a clone.
2. Review basic cloning techniques, including vectors, library construction and screening techniques.
3. Review the DNA sequencing, Southern Analysis and PCR amplification.
4. Be able to design a cloning strategy beginning with understanding what is to be cloned, why it is to be cloned and what will be done with the clone. The cloning strategy consists of the origin of DNA (genomic or cDNA library), choice of cloning vector, and choice of screening technique to recognize clone.

Problem 1

A restriction map provides information as to the presence and position of one or more restriction sites. In many ways it is like the road map to a DNA molecule, and is used in many recombinant DNA techniques.

Digestion with a single enzyme can provide information about the number of restriction sites and the distance between them, but the order of the sites cannot be discerned. However, if a second enzyme is used both alone and in combination with the first enzyme, a map can be constructed.

In this problem, you will determine the restriction map for a linear DNA sample using the enzymes Eco RI and Hind III. Three samples of DNA are first digested with either Eco RI, Hind III or both Eco RI and Hind III. The resulting fragments (restriction fragments) are separated by size using gel electrophoresis.

The results are shown here.

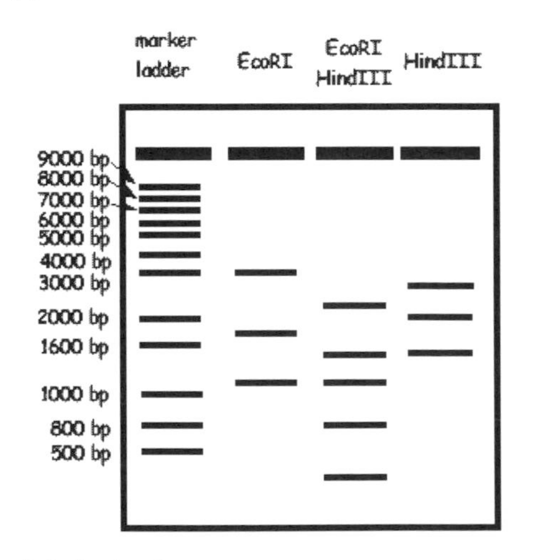

Since the DNA fragments in each lane are derived from the same linear DNA fragment, the sum of the size of fragments in each lane should be the same and reflect the size of the original DNA fragment. How many base pairs are in the original DNA molecule?

Focus first on the Eco RI single digest. Since we know our sample DNA is linear, how many EcoRI sites are present in the DNA?

When the same DNA sample is digested with Eco RI and Hind III, five fragments are generated. Let's look at this one band at a time. Since the 3000 bp Eco RI fragment is not present in the double digest, it must contain at least one Hind III site. Which fragments in the double digest add up to 3000? Which bands in the double digest add up to 1800? Now there is only one fragment left in the double digest. This is the same size as one of the Eco RI fragments in the single digest. It must correspond to the band in the Eco RI lane.

Now, let's focus on the Hind III digest. The largest band, 2500 bp, disappears in the double digest. Which two bands in the double digest add up to 2500 bp? Which two bands in the double digest add up to 2000 bp? That leaves just the 1500 bp Hind III fragment, which is also present in the double digest. This means that there are no Eco RI sites inside this fragment and may indicate the end fragment on a linear DNA.

Since this is a linear DNA fragment, let's start with one of the fragments that is the same in both the single and double digest. This could be an end fragment. Although we could start with either the 1200 or 1500 bp fragment, let's begin with placing the 1200 bp fragment on the left side and build the map from there. Create a map using the information gained from the single and double digests above.

Problem 2

You have just identified a patient who appears to have an altered hemoglobin protein (β-subunit). Analysis of the patient's blood by Southern, northern and western blotting reveals no detectable change of the DNA, a larger RNA and smaller protein. You surmise that the mutation affects hemoglobin splicing. With a clone of the wild type hemoglobin in hand, and cultured skin cells from the patient (as a source of DNA or RNA), select a type of insert, a type of vector and a method in which to identify and study the mutant hemoglobin gene.

Problem 3

After many months in the laboratory, you have finally obtained a pure preparation of DNA polymerase from a novel fungus. However, you have a very limited amount and cannot do all of the biochemical experiments you would like. Your advisor suggests that you use your purified polymerase to clone the gene encoding the polymerase. After consulting several other graduate students, you come up with a plan. Select a type of insert, a type of vector and a method to identify the DNA polymerase gene.

Problem 4

Polydactyly is known to be caused by a dominant allele and is characterized by extra fingers and/or toes. Recently, an RFLP has been identified which is linked to polydactyly and you decide to use this information to clone the gene. Determine what type of insert you would use in making your library, what type of cloning vector would be optimal, and how you would go about identifying the correct clone.